Raintree Steck-Vaughn

Illustrated
SCIENCE
ENCYCLOPEDIA

Volume
17

PRO – RES

RSVP

RAINTREE
STECK-VAUGHN
P U B L I S H E R S

The Steck-Vaughn Company

Austin, Texas

Published by Raintree Steck-Vaughn Publishers, an imprint of Steck-Vaughn Company.

Executive Editor	Diane Sharpe
Senior Editor	Anne Souby
Design Manager	Joyce Spicer

This edition edited and designed by Andromeda Oxford Ltd.

Andromeda Editorial and Design

Project Manager	Julia Roles
Editorial Manager	Jenny Fry
Design	TT Designs, T&S Truscott
Cover Design	John Barker

Library of Congress Cataloging-in-Publication Data
Raintree Steck-Vaughn illustrated science encyclopedia.
        p.   cm.
    Includes bibliographical references and index.
    Summary: A twenty-four volume set containing brief articles on science topics.
    ISBN 0-8172-3943-X (set)
    ISBN 0-8172-3935-9 (Volume 17)
    1. Science—Encyclopedias, Juvenile.   [1. Science—Encyclopedias.]   I. Raintree Steck-Vaughn Publishers.
Q121.R354   1997
503—dc20   96-11078
                                                      CIP
                                                       AC

Printed and Bound in the United States of America.
1 2 3 4 5 6 7 8 9 10 IP 00 99 98 97 96

USING THE RAINTREE STECK-VAUGHN ILLUSTRATED SCIENCE ENCYCLOPEDIA

You are living in a world in which science, technology, and nature are very important. You see something about science almost every day. It might be on television, in the newspaper, in a book at school, or some other place. Often, you want more information about what you see.

The *Raintree Steck-Vaughn Illustrated Science Encyclopedia* will help you find what you want to know. It contains information on many science subjects. You may want to find out about computers, the environment, space exploration, biology, agriculture, or mathematics, for example. They are all in the *Raintree Steck-Vaughn Illustrated Science Encyclopedia.* There are many, many other subjects covered as well.

There are twenty-four volumes in the encyclopedia. The articles, which are called entries, are in alphabetical order through the first twenty-two volumes. On the spine of each volume, below the volume number, are some letters. The letters above the line are the first three letters of the first entry in that volume. The letters below the line are the first three letters of the last entry in that volume. In Volume 1, for example, you see that the first entry begins with **AAR** and that the last entry begins with **ANT**. Using the letters makes it easy to find the volume you need.

In Volume 23, there are three special features—reference charts and tables, a bibliography, and an index. In Volume 24, there are interesting projects that you can do on your own. The projects are fun to do, and they help you discover and understand important science principles. Many can give you ideas that can help you develop your own science fair projects.

Main Entries There are two kinds of main entries in the *Raintree Steck-Vaughn Illustrated Science Encyclopedia.* Many of the entries are major topics that are spread over several pages. The titles of these entries are shown at the top of the page in a yellow box. Other entries required less space to cover the topic fully. The titles of these main entries are printed in capital letters. They look like this: **ABALONE**. At the beginning of some entries, you will see a phonetic pronunciation of the entry title, such as (ăb′ ə lō′ nē).

In the front of each volume, there is a pronunciation key. Use it the same way you use your dictionary's pronunciation key.

Cross-References Within the main entries are cross-references referring to other entries in the encyclopedia. Within an entry, they look like this: (see MAMMAL). At the end of an entry, they look like this: *See also* HYENA. These cross-references tell you where to find other helpful information on the subject you are reading about.

Projects At the end of some entries, you will see this symbol: ⚡ PROJECT 1. It tells you which projects related to that entry are in Volume 24.

Illustrations There are thousands of photographs, drawings, graphs, diagrams, tables, and other illustrations in the *Raintree Steck-Vaughn Illustrated Science Encyclopedia.* They will help you better understand the entries you read. Captions describe the illustrations. Many of the illustrations also have labels that point out important parts.

Activities Some main entries include activities presented in a special box. These activities are short projects that give you a chance to work with science on your own.

Index In Volume 23, the index lists every main entry by volume and page number. Many subjects that are not main entries are also listed in the index, as well as the illustrations, projects, activities, and reference charts and tables.

Bibliography In Volume 23, there is also a bibliography for students. The books in this list are on a variety of topics and can supplement what you have learned in the *Raintree Steck-Vaughn Illustrated Science Encyclopedia.*

The *Raintree Steck-Vaughn Illustrated Science Encyclopedia* was designed especially for you, the student. It is a source of knowledge for the world of science, technology, and nature. Enjoy it!

PRONUNCIATION KEY

Each symbol has the same sound as the darker letters in the sample words.

ə	balloon, ago	îr	deer, pier	r	root, tire
ă	map, have	j	join, germ	s	so, press
ā	day, made	k	king, ask	sh	shoot, machine
âr	care, bear	l	let, cool	t	to, stand
ä	father, car	m	man, same	th	thin, death
b	ball, rib	n	no, turn	*th*	then, this
ch	choose, nature	ng	bring, long	ŭ	up, cut
d	did, add	ŏ	odd, pot	ûr	urge, hurt
ĕ	bell, get	ō	cone, know	v	view, give
ē	sweet, easy	ô	all, saw	w	wood, glowing
f	fan, soft	oi	boy, boil	y	yes, year
g	good, big	ou	now, loud	z	zero, raise
h	hurt, ahead	ŏŏ	good, took	zh	leisure, vision
ĭ	rip, ill	ōō	boot, noon	'	strong accent
ī	side, sky	p	part, scrap	´	weak accent

GUIDE TO MEASUREMENT ABBREVIATIONS

All measurements in the *Raintree Steck-Vaughn Illustrated Science Encyclopedia* are given in both the customary system and the metric system [in brackets like these]. Following are the abbreviations used for various units of measure.

Customary Units of Measure

mi. = miles	cu. yd. = cubic yards
m.p.h. = miles per hour	cu. ft. = cubic feet
yd. = yards	cu. in. = cubic inches
ft. = feet	gal. = gallons
in. = inches	pt. = pints
sq. mi. = square miles	qt. = quarts
sq. yd. = square yards	lb. = pounds
sq. ft. = square feet	oz. = ounces
sq. in. = square inches	fl. oz. = fluid ounces
cu. mi. = cubic miles	°F = degrees Fahrenheit

Metric Units of Measure

km = kilometers	cu. km = cubic kilometers
kph = kilometers per hour	cu. m = cubic meters
m = meters	cu. cm = cubic centimeters
cm = centimeters	ml = milliliters
mm = millimeters	kg = kilograms
sq. km = square kilometers	g = grams
sq. m = square meters	mg = milligrams
sq. cm = square centimeters	°C = degrees Celsius

For information on how to convert customary measurements to metric measurements,
see the Metric Conversions table in Volume 23.

PROTISTA (prō tĭs′ tə) Protista is a kingdom, in the five-kingdom system of classification, that includes one-celled organisms called protozoans and all algae except blue-green algae.

See also ALGAE; CLASSIFICATION OF LIVING ORGANISMS; KINGDOM; PROTOZOA.

PROTON (prō′tŏn′) All matter consists of very tiny particles called atoms. The atom is made up of a central core called the nucleus. Around the nucleus are particles called electrons. The nucleus contains two main kinds of particles: protons and neutrons (see ATOM; NUCLEUS). Because the proton is smaller than the atom, it is called a sub-atomic particle. A proton has a positive electric charge. It spins around its own axis like a spinning ball.

Physicists used to think that the proton had no structure, but they now believe that it does. Physicists think that the proton is made up of three subatomic particles called quarks (see QUARK). Physicists also used to think the proton did not naturally decay (break down) into other particles. They now believe the proton may decay.

The sun sends large numbers of protons out into space. Some of these protons reach the earth. Because they have an electric charge, they become trapped in the earth's magnetic field. These trapped protons help form a belt of radiation around the earth. Other particles from the sun form another belt around the earth. These two belts are Van Allen belts.

See also PARTICLE PHYSICS; VAN ALLEN BELTS.

PROTOPLASM (prō′tə plăz′əm) The term *protoplasm* refers to the living matter of cells. *Protoplasm* comes from the Greek words *protos*, meaning "first," and *plasma*, meaning "form." Scientists generally use more specific terms, such as *cytoplasm, ectoplasm,* or *endoplasm,* when discussing the cell.

See also CELL.

PROTOZOA (prō′tə zō′ə) Protozoa is a group of one-celled organisms, most of which are microscopic. Protozoans belong to kingdom Protista (see CELL; PROTISTA). There are about thirty thousand identified species of living protozoans. There are undoubtedly many more unidentified species, and many other species that are now extinct (see EXTINCTION). Protozoans are found throughout the world.

Protozoans range in size from the smallest, a parasite in red blood cells that measures 0.00008 in. [0.0002 cm] in diameter, to the largest, a radiolarian measuring 0.2 in. [0.5 cm] in diameter (see PARASITE; RADIOLARIAN). Protozoans live in many environments. Most live in water. Some live in the soil, while others live in the bodies of other organisms. Protozoans make up a large part of the zooplankton found in the oceans (see PLANKTON).

Kinds of protozoans Some protozoans are simple in structure. Others are among the most complex cells known. The protozoans are usually divided into four groups, according to the way that they move from one place to another: the flagellates; the sarcodines; the sporozoans; and the ciliates.

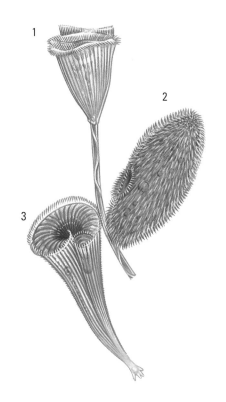

PROTOZOA—Ciliates

Ciliates are named for their tiny, hairlike cilia. The organisms beat the cilia rapidly in order to move around or to create water currents that bring them food particles. The ciliates pictured are (1) *Vorticella*, (2) a paramecium, and (3) *Stentor*.

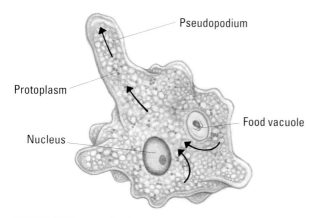

PROTOZOA—Ameboid movement

An ameba moves by extending a pseudopodium (meaning "false foot"), into which the organism's protoplasm flows.

The flagellates are the most primitive of the protozoans. They have one or more long, whiplike flagella with which they propel themselves (see FLAGELLATE; FLAGELLUM). Flagellates are usually oval in shape. Many flagellates live in the bodies of other organisms, often as parasites. One of these, *Trypanosoma gambiense,* causes African sleeping sickness (see SLEEPING SICKNESS; TRYPANOSOME).

The sarcodines are protozoans that move by ameboid movement. In ameboid movement, the organism sends out pseudopodia, or "false feet." These pseudopodia are masses of protoplasm that let the organism "ooze" from one place to another (see PROTOPLASM). The most familiar sarcodinian is the ameba (see AMEBA). Many sarcodines live in the bodies of human beings and other animals. Some are parasites, while others live symbiotically (see SYMBIOSIS). One kind of ameba causes amebic dysentery, a serious infection of the human digestive system.

The sarcodines include two organisms that contribute to geological formations: the radiolarians and the foraminifers. The radiolarians have skeletons made of silica that pile up on the ocean floor when the organisms die. The foraminifers have horny, glossy, or chalky shells that also pile up on the ocean floor. All these remains help form the muddy deposits on the ocean floors known as ooze (see OOZE). The foraminifers' shells are also a major constituent of chalk (see CHALK).

The sporozoans are tiny protozoans that usually reproduce by scattering large numbers of spores

(see SPORE). They are all parasites and they generally have very limited powers of movement. The best known of the sporozoans is *Plasmodium,* the malaria-causing protozoan (see MALARIA; PLASMODIUM).

The ciliates are the most complex of the protozoans. They have tiny, hairlike cilia that help them move about in search of food, although many species remain fixed in one place and rely on their cilia to bring currents of water to them (see CILIUM). The ciliates have two nuclei (plural of *nucleus*). The large macronucleus controls cellular activity and asexual reproduction. The smaller micronucleus works in sexual reproduction (see REPRODUCTION). Some ciliates have special structures for getting food. For example, the paramecium has a ciliated oral groove that directs food into the mouth (see PARAMECIUM). Another ciliate, the *Vorticella,* creates a tiny whirlpool to bring food into its mouth.

Protozoan structure and function The free-living protozoans digest food in enzyme-containing structures called food vacuoles (see ENZYME). Many protozoans have contractile vacuoles, which are special structures that squirt wastes and excess water out of the cell.

Most protozoans move away from foreign objects, bright light, chemicals, and very hot or very cold areas. This is a primitive type of response and is called avoidance. It is different from the nervous system response of higher organisms. Some protozoans have a bright red "eye-spot," which may be sensitive to light.

Protozoans usually reproduce asexually by fission (see ASEXUAL REPRODUCTION). In fission, an

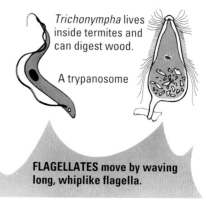

Trichonympha lives inside termites and can digest wood.

A trypanosome

FLAGELLATES move by waving long, whiplike flagella.

organism splits into two new organisms. Some protozoans reproduce asexually by budding (see BUDDING). Some (the sporozoans) reproduce by releasing large numbers of spores. Others undergo a primitive kind of sexual reproduction. In this process, two organisms join together, exchange nuclear material, separate, and then divide by fission. This kind of reproduction occurs mainly in the ciliates.

If environmental conditions begin to threaten protozoans, some are able to survive by excreting water, thickening their cell walls, and going into a dormant state (see DORMANCY). In this form, the protozoan is called a cyst. The cyst can survive very hot or very cold conditions. It can live without water or oxygen for long periods of time. Cysts are transported from one place to another by the wind or by becoming attached to animals. As soon as the cyst reaches suitable conditions, it opens to release one or more protozoans. The amebas causing amebic dysentery form very tough cysts when they pass out of the body, and they can cause the disease in anyone who swallows them in food or water.

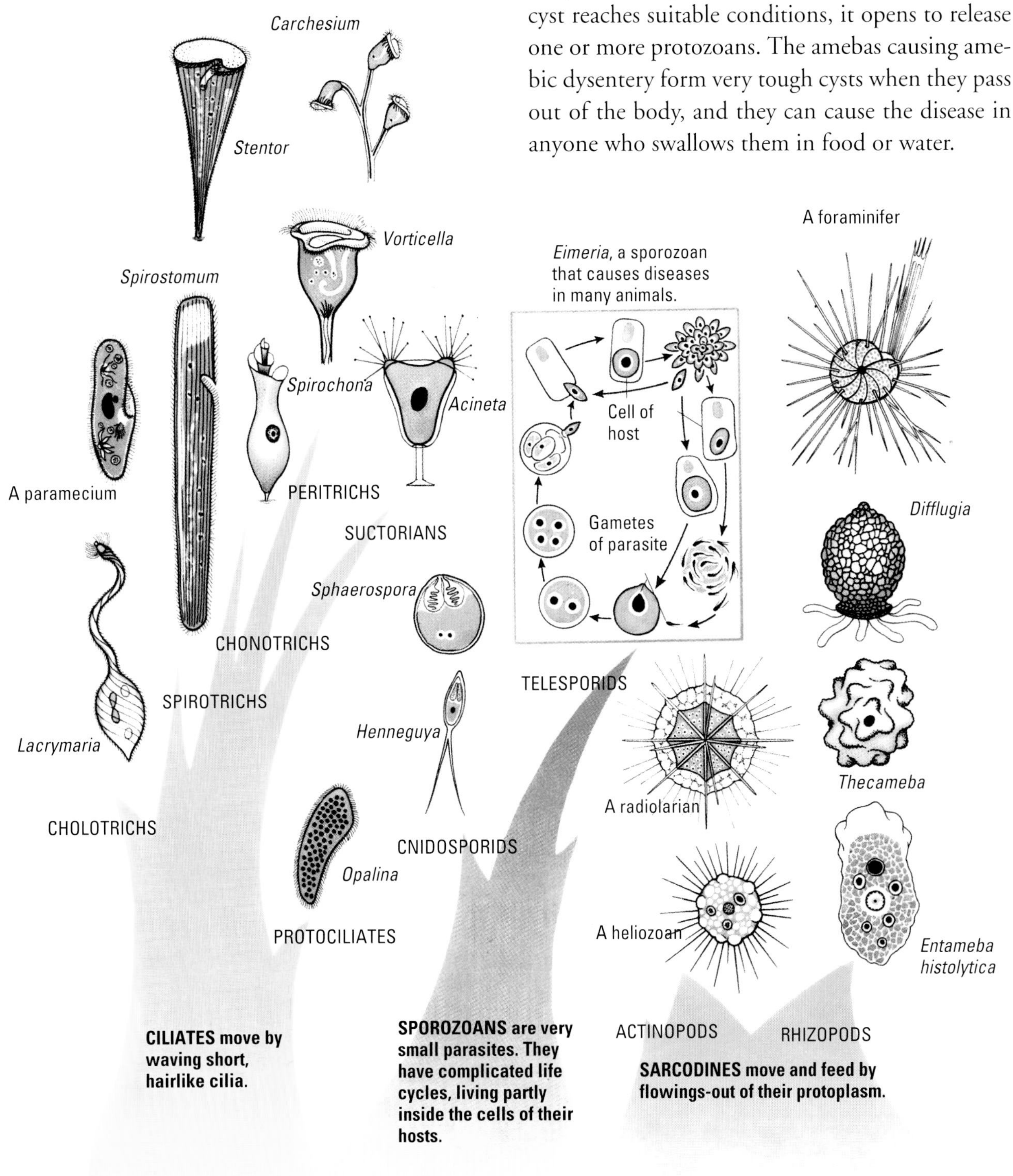

Carchesium

Stentor

Spirostomum

Vorticella

Spirochona

Acineta

A paramecium

PERITRICHS

SUCTORIANS

Sphaerospora

CHONOTRICHS

SPIROTRICHS

Lacrymaria

CHOLOTRICHS

Henneguya

CNIDOSPORIDS

Opalina

PROTOCILIATES

Eimeria, a sporozoan that causes diseases in many animals.

Cell of host

Gametes of parasite

TELESPORIDS

A foraminifer

Difflugia

Thecameba

A radiolarian

A heliozoan

Entameba histolytica

ACTINOPODS

RHIZOPODS

CILIATES move by waving short, hairlike cilia.

SPOROZOANS are very small parasites. They have complicated life cycles, living partly inside the cells of their hosts.

SARCODINES move and feed by flowings-out of their protoplasm.

PSILOPHYTE (sī′lə fīt′) The psilophytes are the most primitive of the vascular plants (see VASCULAR PLANT). The vascular plants have special structures for moving food and water from one part of the plant to another. During the Paleozoic era, about 400 million years ago, the psilophytes were quite common, but today all but two genera (plural of *genus*) of psilophytes are extinct (see EXTINCTION; PALEOZOIC ERA). These surviving plants are mostly tropical. They belong to the pteridophyte group and are thus related to the ferns.

Psilophytes do not have true roots. Instead, they have rootlike stems called rhizomes (see RHIZOME). These may grow under the ground, but are more often anchored in rock crevices or in the bark of trees. The aboveground stems are green and have many tiny openings called stomata (see STOMA). Most photosynthesis in these plants takes place in the stems (see PHOTOSYNTHESIS). The leaves are scaly or spinelike, or missing altogether. They contain very little chlorophyll (see CHLOROPHYLL).

Psilophytes undergo alternation of generations (see ALTERNATION OF GENERATIONS). The sporophyte, or asexual stage, is prominent. Its spores grow into tiny, saprophytic plants called prothalli (see SAPROPHYTE). The prothalli are the gametophytes. Frequently, the prothalli live symbiotically with a type of fungus (see FUNGUS; SYMBIOSIS). The prothalli produce male gametes, or sperm, in antheridia, and female gametes, or eggs, in archegonia. After fertilization, the zygotes grow into new sporophytes.
See also PALEOBOTANY; PLANT KINGDOM.

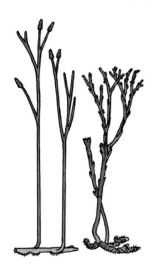

PSILOPHYTE

Psilophytes are known from fossils of the Silurian period. The drawing at far left is a reconstruction of *Zosterophyllum*, which appears to have been a very simple plant. Sporangia (structures that produce spores) can be seen at the tips of the branches. The drawing at near left is of *Psilotum*, a modern psilophyte.

PSYCHIATRY (sĭ kī′ə trē) Psychiatry is the branch of medicine concerned with the treatment and prevention of mental illness. A psychiatrist is a person who, after being trained as a physician, or medical doctor, trains for three or more years in the treatment of mental illness (see DOCTOR; MENTAL ILLNESS).

Psychiatrists use several basic methods to treat persons with mental illness. One method is called psychotherapy. Psychotherapy mainly involves discussions between the patient and the psychiatrist. The patient discusses his or her problems with the psychiatrist. In turn, the psychiatrist tries to build the patient's confidence and help the patient develop better methods for coping with life and its stresses. Some psychiatrists use hypnotism to help them understand the patient's problems (see HYPNOSIS). Sometimes groups of patients take part in "group therapy." Such patients, meeting as a group with the psychiatrist, help each other understand themselves. The psychiatrist may try to get the patients to act out their problems in little plays called "psychodramas." When working with a child, a psychiatrist often uses "play therapy." In play therapy, instead of the child trying to talk about a problem, the child acts it out with games or toys.

Psychoanalysis is often used to guide psychotherapy. Psychoanalysis is based on the theory that the causes of many mental illnesses are buried in the unconscious. A patient may have no idea what is causing the problems. The psychiatrist, by uncovering the causes, is given an indication of which treatment to use, and helps the patient better understand himself or herself (see PSYCHOANALYSIS).

Behavioral therapy is another basic method used by psychiatrists. In this kind of therapy, rewards and punishments are used to help patients change their behavior in healthy ways.

Drug therapy sometimes gives help for certain kinds of mental illnesses, especially some types of depression and psychoses. Tranquilizers are drugs that help calm a patient. Sedatives help relieve nervousness or anxiety (see SEDATIVE; TRANQUILIZER).

Whatever treatment, or combination of treatments, psychiatrists use depends on various factors, such as the type, cause, and extent of the mental illness.

See also FREUD, SIGMUND; JUNG, CARL GUSTAV; PSYCHOLOGY; PSYCHOSOMATIC DISORDER.

PSYCHOANALYSIS (sī′kō ə năl′ĭ sĭs) Psycho-

analysis is used to guide psychotherapy in treating mental illness. A psychoanalyst is a person, often a psychiatrist, who has had several years of training in psychoanalytic principles (see MENTAL ILLNESS; PSYCHIATRY; PSYCHOLOGY). Psychoanalysis was developed in the late 1800s and early 1900s by Sigmund Freud, an Austrian psychiatrist and psychologist (see FREUD, SIGMUND). Other psychiatrists developed variations of Freud's technique.

PSYCHOANALYSIS
The Austrian psychiatrist and pyschologist Sigmund Freud was the founder of psychoanalysis.

Psychoanalysis is based on the theory that unpleasant experiences, especially during childhood, may become buried in a person's unconscious (nonthinking) mind and cause mental illness. Psychoanalysis tries to bring the unpleasant experiences out of the patient's unconscious and into his or her conscious mind. By doing this, the patient may be able to understand the cause of his or her problems. This understanding often helps the patient better adjust to life.

Psychoanalytic treatment usually includes a method of "free association" to search a patient's unconscious and discover the cause of illness. In this method, the patient relaxes on a bed or couch. The psychoanalyst tries to get the patient to talk about anything that comes to his or her mind. Sometimes, the patient's dreams are discussed.

Dreams may give clues to the patient's unconscious (see DREAM). In some cases, a psychoanalyst may use hypnosis to help gain insight into the patient's unconscious (see HYPNOSIS). Sessions of psychoanalysis may take place several times each week for months, or possibly years.

The patient may find it difficult to talk freely with the psychoanalyst at first. However, when the patient begins to trust the psychoanalyst, the analyst usually can help the patient understand his or her inner problems.

Psychoanalysis is used most often for patients with mild mental disorders.

See also PSYCHOLOGY.

PSYCHOLOGY (sī kŏl′ə jē) Psychology is the

branch of science concerned with why human beings and other animals behave as they do. The word *psychology* comes from the Greek words *psyche,* meaning "mind," and *logos,* meaning "study of." Psychology is a very broad science. Studies in psychology range from the ability of mice to learn the path through a maze to the causes of international tensions. Most psychologists have a master's or doctoral degree in psychology.

Psychologists are interested in all animal experience—how creatures learn to perform various tasks; how they solve problems; how their senses work; and what the reasons are for various thoughts and feelings. Although psychologists have learned much about behavior and experience, there is still a great deal to be discovered in this field.

Psychology is frequently grouped with biology, sociology, and anthropology as one of the behavioral sciences. Psychology is also related to psychiatry (see PSYCHIATRY).

History Psychology was once a field of study within philosophy. In ancient times, Plato, Aristotle, and other philosophers developed theories about the causes of behavior and the relationships between mind and body.

Psychology became established as a science in 1879, when Wilhelm Wundt set up the first psychological laboratory in Leipzig, Germany. From the late 1800s until the 1930s, four different ways of studying the mind were developed. These methods, or "schools," of psychology are structuralism, behaviorism, gestalt psychology, and psychoanalysis.

Structural psychologists, such as Wundt, believed the main purpose of psychology was to describe and analyze the way people experience or perceive things through their senses. For instance, the sense of sight gives the mind a great deal of information, including color, size, shape, and distance. The sense of touch gives information about texture, heat, cold, pain, and so on. Structural psychologists wanted to find out what kind of information the mind was getting. Introspection was the chief method that these psychologists used. Introspection takes place when a person observes his or her own experiences when stimulated by some object or event.

In 1913, John B. Watson, an American psychologist, introduced behaviorism into psychology. Behaviorism was a reaction against the structural method of introspection. Watson called for psychologists to study the behavior of people and other animals. Behavioral psychologists began laboratory experiments on the way people and other animals behave in various situations. For example, Ivan Pavlov conducted experiments on the reflexes of dogs (see PAVLOV, IVAN). Behavioral psychologists continued these experiments to find out how people or other animals usually behave. They tried to determine if behavior can be changed and how it can be changed.

About 1912, Max Wertheimer began developing

PSYCHOLOGY— Ivan Pavlov

The Soviet psychologist Ivan Pavlov helped establish behavioral psychology with his studies of conditioned reflexes in dogs.

gestalt psychology in Germany. In the 1930s, Wertheimer and his associates moved to the United States, where they headed the gestalt movement. *Gestalt* is a German word meaning "pattern" or "form." Gestalt psychologists believed that people perceive things in patterns or groups, not in individual parts that they then put together. For example, if people look at an automobile, they see all at once a whole object that has windows, doors, tires, and so on. They do not first see each tire, each door, and each window separately. Gestalt psychologists created tests to determine patterns of perception (the ability to be aware of things and understand them through the senses, especially sight). The most famous of these tests is the inkblot test. In such a test, a person describes what he or she sees in the inkblot. Gestalt psychologists attacked the view of structural psychologists that experience could be broken down into its parts, such as seeing, hearing, and touching. Gestalt psychologists believed that all these processes must be studied together in order to understand how people actually think and perceive things (see WERTHEIMER, MAX).

Psychoanalysis began in the early 1900s with the work of Sigmund Freud (see FREUD, SIGMUND; PSYCHOANALYSIS). According to Freud, people tend to repress (push out of the conscious, thinking mind) any thoughts or memories that they or other people do not approve of. These repressed thoughts have a great effect on people's behavior. Although many psychologists today do not agree with many of Freud's statements, Freud is given credit for showing how the unconscious mind can influence behavior.

Branches of psychology Today, psychology is divided into several major specialties. Experimental psychology is concerned with laboratory research on humans and other animals to find out what causes specific behaviors. Physiological psychology is concerned with the relationship between behavior and the function of the nervous system. The psychology of learning deals with how people learn, that is, how people get ideas and put them to use.

PSYCHOLOGY—Educational psychology
Educational psychologists use intelligence tests to estimate the development of reasoning skills in young children.

One branch of the psychology of learning, called educational psychology, studies the problems of learning in schools. Another branch, called cognitive psychology, studies how people process information and store and retrieve information in their memory (see LEARNING AND MEMORY). Child psychology is the study of the growth and development of children.

The psychology of individual differences is concerned with discovering why people act in the same way as or differently from each other. Psychologists in this field have developed many different kinds of tests to find out about people's individual characteristics (see PSYCHOMETRIC TESTING).

Abnormal psychology is the study of mental or emotional problems. Psychologists, often working with psychiatrists, try to find out the causes of these problems and suggest ways of working them out. Social psychologists study the behavior of people in groups. For example, a social psychologist may study how a group of sixth-graders behaves toward a group of third-graders. Personnel or industrial psychologists try to discover what kind of job a

person is suited for. They try to help workers who have problems in getting along with other workers.

Psychology in daily living To understand why we behave as we do and how we experience things is of great importance in our daily lives. Such an understanding helps people understand themselves and their feelings. By learning to understand themselves, people can lessen their worries and fears and adapt to various situations.

People also want to discover their skills and aptitudes. Such factors can help them in selecting a career that could make them happy. Understanding human behavior helps people teach children, both at home and in school, and can also guide them in getting along better with each other. Psychology is also widely used by advertisers to try to persuade people to buy their product, and by political organizations to try to gauge and influence what people think about the organization.

See also EMOTION; INSTINCT; INTELLIGENCE; MENTAL ILLNESS; PIAGET, JEAN.

PSYCHOMETRIC TESTING Psychometric testing is used by psychologists to give a systematic measurement of mental processes or behavior (see PSYCHOLOGY). Some tests measure a person's interests (likes and dislikes). Others measure how well a person does in comparison with other people of the same age and similar background. Some tests measure aptitude (things for which a person has a particular talent), personality, achievements (what a person has learned so far), and attitudes (opinions).

Some psychometric tests measure people's responses to physical objects or stimuli in controlled laboratory conditions. Most psychometric tests, however, are designed to measure how people think using scales of preference or ability. The person rates what he or she thinks about a certain question or task. For example, 1 could mean "excellent" or "strongly agree" and 5 "very poor" or "strongly disagree," with values in-between standing for less strong opinions. How people rate themselves on the scale can then be used to show their attributes and opinions compared with others, or to uncover emotions or mental conflict. Groups of people can be tested using the survey or questionnaire method. Psychologists can receive sets of answers to a standard questionnaire and so learn about the characteristics, interests, or achievements of that particular group.

PSYCHOSOMATIC DISORDER (sī′kə sō măt′ĭk dĭs ôr′dər) A psychosomatic disorder is a physical illness that is caused or chiefly influenced by the emotional state of the person. The term *psychosomatic* comes from the Greek words *psyche,* meaning "mind," and *soma,* meaning "of the body."

Physicians know that emotional disturbances often affect a person's body. For example, when a person is angry or afraid, a certain hormone flows into the blood and speeds up the action of the heart (see EMOTION; HORMONE).

There are various physical illnesses that seem to be associated with emotional disturbances. Among these are asthma, stomach ulcers, rheumatoid arthritis (stiffness of the bone joints), hypertension (high blood pressure), and some types of obesity (overweight). Disorders in which mental problems can cause physical symptoms, such as apparent paralysis of an arm, are not considered psychosomatic. This is because the "paralyzed" arm has nothing physically wrong with it. The nerves and muscles are capable of working normally, but a mental problem prevents this. Psychosomatic disorders require both medical treatment and psychiatric treatment.
See also MEDICINE; PSYCHIATRY.

PTERIDOPHYTE (tə rĭd′ə fīt′) The pteridophytes are a large group of flowerless vascular plants (see VASCULAR PLANT). They include the ferns, horsetails, and club mosses (see CLUB MOSS; FERN; HORSETAIL). Although these plants do not have flowers, they do have true roots, stems, and leaves. Giant species of these plants grew in great forests about 250 million years ago, near the end of the Paleozoic era (see PALEOZOIC ERA).

With the exception of some tropical tree ferns, the living pteridophytes are small herbaceous plants (see HERBACEOUS PLANT). The pteridophytes, like many other lower plants, undergo alternation of generations.
See also ALTERNATION OF GENERATIONS; PLANT KINGDOM.

PTERIDOPHYTE
Pteridophytes are a group of simple plants that include ferns (top) and horsetails (above and left).

PTERODACTYLUS (tĕr′ə dăk′təl əs) *Ptero-dactylus* is a genus of prehistoric winged reptiles known as pterosaurs (see PTEROSAUR). *Pterodactyl* is a shortened form of the name that used to refer to pterosaurs. Pterosaurs existed from the late Triassic period to the end of the Cretaceous period (220 to 65 million years ago). Modern birds are not descended from the pterodactyls.

Pterosaurs with short tails are known as ptero-dactyloids. Pterodactyloids existed during the Jurassic and Cretaceous periods (150 to 65 million years ago). The reason for the extinction of ptero-dactyloids at the end of the Cretaceous period is uncertain.

See also DINOSAUR.

PTEROSAUR (tĕr′ə sôr′) The pterosaurs were a group of winged reptiles that existed at the time of the dinosaurs, from the late Triassic period to the end of the Cretaceous period (220 to 65 million years ago). Although they were not dinosaurs, they were closely related. Modern birds are not descended from pterosaurs.

Pterosaurs were very active, flapping their wings like birds rather than gliding like flying squirrels. However, the pterosaur's wings were like a bat's wings. Each wing had four fingers. The first three fingers were short and used for grasping. The fourth finger was long and supported the animal's membranous wing. The wingspan of pterosaurs ranged from 1 to 50 ft. [0.3 to 15.5 m].

The earliest pterosaurs had narrow wings and a long tail. One long-tailed pterosaur is *Rham-phorhynchus*, a seagull-sized pterosaur from late Jurassic times. Some later pterosaurs had short tails. Perhaps the best known of these short-tailed types is *Pterodactylus*, which was about the same size as *Rhamphorhynchus* and lived at the same time (see PTERODACTYLUS). The name, shortened to "ptero-dactyl," used to be the popular name for the whole pterosaur group.

Pterosaurs came in a great many sizes and shapes. Some, like *Batrachognathus*, were about the size of sparrows and ate insects. Others, like the late Cretaceous *Quetzalcoatlus* and *Arambourgiana*, were the size of small airplanes and probably ate fish.

PTEROSAUR—Different types

Pterodactylus and *Anurognathus* were short-tailed pterosaurs. In contrast, *Peteinosaurus* and *Rhamphorhynchus* had long, reptilelike tails.

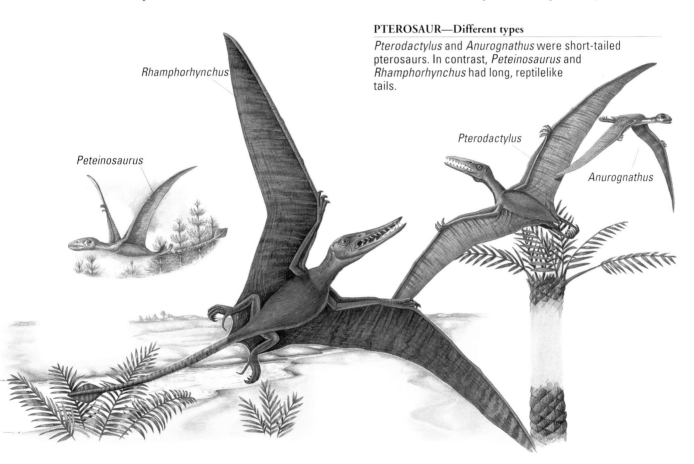

Rhamphorhynchus

Peteinosaurus

Pterodactylus

Anurognathus

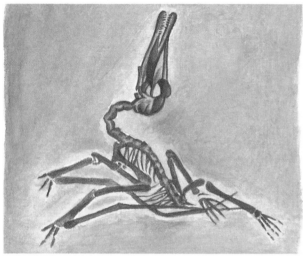

PTEROSAUR—Fossil

Sometimes scientists find a fossil of a complete pterosaur skeleton, such as this one (above). The head became turned back as the animal's body dried out before it was buried.

Pterosaurs were covered with hair like modern bats, showing that they were probably warm-blooded like mammals rather than cold-blooded like other reptiles. The reason for their extinction at the end of the Cretaceous period is uncertain.

PTOLEMY (tŏl′ə mē) Ptolemy was a Greek scientist who lived in the second century A.D. Very little is known about his life. Even the years of his birth and death are not known. Ptolemy studied astronomy, mathematics, and geography. He named forty-eight of the eighty-eight constellations recognized today (see CONSTELLATION).

Ptolemy wrote a series of books called the *Almagest.* These books contained all that was known about astronomy at that time. In the *Almagest,* Ptolemy presented his system of the universe. He thought that the earth was at the center of the universe, and all the objects in the universe

revolved around the earth. Ptolemy's system was accepted for more than one thousand years, until Copernicus developed the theory that the earth revolved around the sun (see COPERNICUS).

Ptolemy also wrote a book on geography. In this book, the idea of latitude and longitude was introduced for the first time.
See also LATITUDE AND LONGITUDE.

PUBERTY (pyōō′ bər tē) Puberty is the period of rapid physical changes in humans that mark the end of childhood and the attainment of sexual maturity. Puberty begins the stage known as adolescence and usually occurs at about age eleven or twelve (see ADOLESCENCE). However, puberty may begin at different times for different people. For example, puberty may occur as early as age ten or as late as the middle teens. After puberty, boys and girls have the ability to reproduce (see REPRODUCTION).

Males generally enter puberty at about age twelve. During puberty, their testicles grow larger and begin to produce the hormone testosterone (see HORMONE; TESTICLE). This hormone causes the body to become heavier, stronger, and taller; the shoulders to broaden; and the voice to deepen. Increased testosterone and other androgens that are produced by the adrenal glands also cause hair to grow on the face, under the arms, and around the genitals (sex organs). Many males at this age also begin to experience "wet dreams," or spontaneous nighttime ejaculations of semen (the fluid that contains sperm).

Puberty generally begins in females at about age eleven. During puberty, the ovaries begin to produce increased amounts of the hormone estrogen. Estrogen causes the ovaries and the uterus to mature, the breasts to enlarge, and the hips to widen (see OVARY; UTERUS). Androgens cause hair to grow under the arms and around the genitals (see REPRODUCTIVE SYSTEM). By about age twelve, the first menstrual cycle occurs.

See also MENSTRUAL CYCLE.

PUFF ADDER

The puff adder gets its name from its habit of puffing air out of its mouth before striking its prey.

PUFF ADDER The puff adder is a poisonous snake that belongs to the viper family, Viperidae (see VIPER). It is a thick, large-headed snake that can reach several feet in length. The puff adder eats lizards and small mammals. There are many species of puff adders. They live in the forests, deserts, and grasslands of Africa. They are called puff adders because they puff out air with a hissing sound before they strike.

See also ADDER; SNAKE.

PUFFIN A puffin is a seabird that belongs to the auk family, Alcidae (see AUK). It is a stocky bird with a short tail and wings. The puffin grows to 11 to 12.5 in. [27.5 to 30 cm] in length. It has an unusually large, orange and yellow bill; a white face; and a dark brown back and wings. Three species of puffins live off the coasts of North America. The horned puffin and the tufted puffin live in the North Pacific Ocean, while the common puffin lives in the North Atlantic Ocean. All three species spend most of the time on the open ocean, where they feed on fish, especially sand eels, and other small sea creatures. They can dive deeply,

PUFFIN

The puffin (above) uses its colorful bill to carry fish, such as sand eels, which it catches in coastal seas. On land, puffins form large colonies (left), making nests in burrows.

using their wings to swim under the water. They come ashore only to breed. When they are breeding, puffins are found in large numbers on rocky islands and coastlines.

PULLEY A pulley is a simple machine that consists of a grooved wheel, or a group of grooved wheels, around which a rope or chain can be run (see MACHINE, SIMPLE). One end of the rope is pulled to lift a weight at the other end. A simple pulley consists of a single pulley wheel over which a rope or chain runs. This type of pulley is used to lift a load (see LOAD). It does not reduce the force needed to lift the load but changes the direction in which the force needs be applied to a more convenient direction (see FORCE). The use of more than one pulley wheel magnifies the force applied (called the effort) so that a heavier load can be lifted by a

PULLEY

Pulleys are important parts of cranes. Pulleys change the direction of the lifting force and provide mechanical advantage.

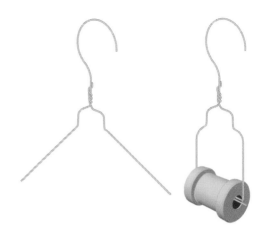

ACTIVITY   *Make a pulley*

Cut both ends of a wire coat hanger about 8 in. [20 cm] from the hook. Bend the ends at right angles and slip them through a spool. Hang a string, with a weight attached to one end, over the spool. See how much force is needed to lift the weight.
Caution: Be very careful when cutting the wire.

smaller force. In this case, the pulley system is said to have a mechanical advantage of greater than one.

The mechanical advantage depends upon the arrangement of the pulley wheels. For instance, an arrangement with two ropes supporting the load will lift it with half the effort needed to lift it directly (if friction is ignored). This arrangement is said to have a mechanical advantage of 2. A pulley arrangement that has four ropes supporting the load will have a mechanical advantage of 4. This means that the pulleys will lift the load with one-fourth of the effort needed to lift the load directly. **PROJECT 50**

PULSAR A pulsar is a star that gives off rhythmic pulses of radio waves and other forms of electromagnetic radiation. Pulsars are generally believed to be rapidly spinning neutron stars (see ELECTROMAGNETIC RADIATION; NEUTRON STAR; STAR). *Pulsar* stands for "pulsating radio star." British astronomers discovered the first pulsar in 1967 (see ASTRONOMY). Today, about five hundred pulsars have been discovered.

Pulsars give off radiation at a very regular rate, varying from one pulse every few seconds to a few

PULSAR

These X-ray images of the Crab Nebula show it with its central pulsar "on" (below) and "off" (below right). The pulsar is thought to be a rapidly spinning neutron star.

thousand pulses per second. Astronomers think that younger pulsars give off more rapid pulses than older pulsars.

The most famous pulsar is in the Crab Nebula (see CRAB NEBULA). This pulsar pulsates about thirty times per second. This rate is decreasing slightly each year.

PULSE The pulse is the wave of pressure that passes through the body's arteries every time the heart contracts to pump the blood (see ARTERY; BLOOD; HEART). The pulse can be felt by placing fingers on the wrist above the thumb. The pulse can also be felt by touching the temples or other locations on the body where an artery is near the surface of the skin.

Pulse rates change with age. The pulse rate of a child is faster than that of the average healthy adult. Older people often have a slower pulse rate than younger adults. The average pulse rate for an adult male is 72 beats per minute. The average pulse rate for an adult female is 78 beats per minute. The average rate for a seven-year-old child is 90 beats per minute. A newborn baby can have a pulse rate of 140 beats per minute. Older adults can have pulse rates that range between 50 and 65 beats per minute.

See also CIRCULATORY SYSTEM.

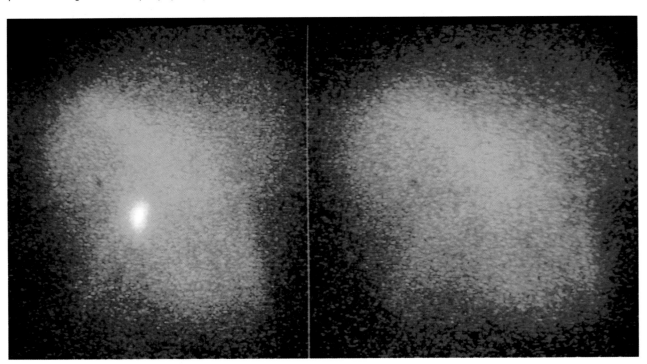

PUMA (pyoo′mə) The puma is a large, wild mammal belonging to the cat family (see CAT). Pumas live throughout the Americas, from Canada to Patagonia (the southern part of South America). These animals can live in deserts, mountains, or forests.

The puma is called by several other names, including *mountain lion, cougar, catamount,* and *panther.* The name *panther* is also given to several other types of cats.

The adult puma generally looks like a female lion. It may be either gray, reddish, or yellowish in color. Some pumas are solid black. A full-grown puma may be 5 ft. [1.5 m] long, not including its long tail. The females have from one to six cubs at a time. Litters (young born at one time) are usually two years apart.

Pumas often hunt at night. The animals are famous for their stamina and strength. They can run great distances while hunting. The puma's main food is deer. Pumas may carry their victims slung over their backs. They often feed on old and diseased deer. In this way, they help keep the populations of deer in a healthy state.

PUMA

The puma is a large member of the cat family that lives throughout the Americas. Many live in mountainous areas, where they are known as mountain lions.

PUMICE (pŭm′ĭs) Pumice is a lightweight, gray-colored rock containing many tiny holes (see ROCK). It is used for polishing, scouring, and scrubbing, either as a powder or in pieces. In the home, pieces of pumice are sometimes used for removing stains or calluses (hard skin) from the hands and feet. These pieces are known as pumice stone.

Pumice is a type of volcanic rock. When a volcano erupts, it throws out molten lava (see LAVA; VOLCANO). Pumice is formed when acidic lava cools and hardens very quickly. Lava contains volcanic gases. When lava cools quickly, these gases become trapped. The trapped gases form bubbles that leave holes in the rock. This is how the holes form in pumice. Because pumice has so many holes, it is often light enough to float in water. Sometimes, solid lumps of pumice are blown out of volcanoes during explosions. This happened during the famous Krakatoa explosion in 1883. Sailors reported seeing large masses of pumice floating in the ocean.

PUMP A pump is a machine that is used for transferring fluids from one place to another. A

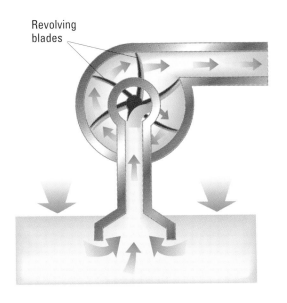

Revolving blades

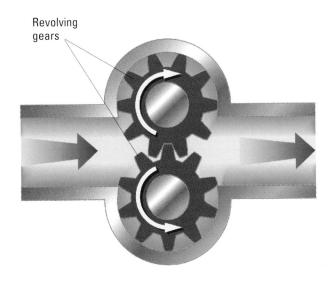

Revolving gears

PUMP—Centrifugal and rotary pumps

In a centrifugal pump (above), the fluid being pumped is fed to the center of a set of revolving blades. It is flung outward by the blades and discharged. In a gear pump (above right), a type of rotary pump, the fluid is carried around by a pair of gear wheels and forced out at the other side of the casing.

fluid can be either a gas or a liquid. There are four main kinds of pumps: the reciprocating pump, the rotary pump, the centrifugal pump, and the vacuum pump.

The simplest reciprocating pump is a bicycle pump. A bicycle pump has a piston that is attached to a handle. A piston is a cylinder that moves up and down inside a larger cylinder. As the piston is pulled up the larger cylinder, air is sucked in through a valve. Then the piston is pushed back down in the cylinder. The force of the air closes the valve, and the air is pumped into the tire. This is called a single-acting pump.

Some reciprocating pumps have a valve on each

PUMP—Reciprocating pump

A lift pump is a type of reciprocating pump. As the handle of a lift pump is pushed down, the piston goes up, and the pressure of the air outside forces water into the cylinder through a valve at the bottom (below). The handle is then pulled up, and water flows through a valve in the piston. The handle is pushed down again, the piston rises, and the valve in the piston closes. This pushes water out of the spout of the pump, as more water fills the space below the piston.

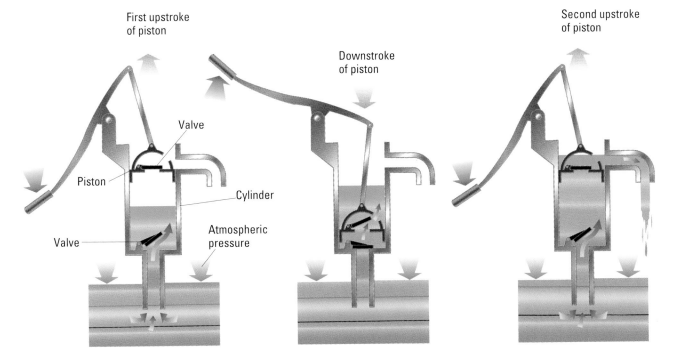

First upstroke of piston

Downstroke of piston

Second upstroke of piston

Valve

Piston

Cylinder

Valve

Atmospheric pressure

side of the piston. Then the piston pumps fluid when it is moving in either direction. This produces a more even flow of fluid. This is called a double-acting pump. Another example of a reciprocating pump is the lift pump. This is the type of pump used for pumping water from wells.

In a rotary pump, the fluid is transferred by a rotary (turning on an axis like a wheel) device. A gear pump is one kind of rotary pump. A gear pump contains two gear wheels that interlock. These wheels turn around inside a casing. The fluid is carried around the gears in the spaces between the teeth. In this way, the fluid is transferred from one side of the gears to the other. The gear pump works well for heavy liquids, but it does not work well for gases. Gear pumps are widely used in the petroleum industry. Other kinds of rotary pumps have spinning blades instead of gear wheels.

Centrifugal pumps contain a motor-driven fan-shaped device called an impeller. The impeller spins around very rapidly as fluid is fed into the middle of it. The fluid is then flung outward by the vanes of the impeller into the chamber. Usually, centrifugal pumps contain a number of impellers, perhaps twenty or more.

The vacuum pump is widely used in industry for emptying containers of fluid. When a fluid, such as steam, flows through a pipe, it travels faster where the pipe narrows. When a fluid travels faster, its pressure decreases. Therefore, the pressure of a fluid decreases when it flows through a narrower pipe. This principle is used in a vacuum pump. A pipe of variable width is placed in a container of liquid or other fluid. Steam enters the pipe and then flows into a narrow section. The narrow part of the pipe contains many tiny holes. As the steam flows through the narrow section, its pressure decreases. This causes the fluid in the container to be sucked in through the small holes. In this way, the fluid is pumped out of the container.

PUPA (pyoo'pə) The pupa is the nonfeeding, usually nonmoving stage in the development of certain insects. The pupal stage follows the larval stage in complete metamorphosis (see LARVA; METAMORPHOSIS). The pupa makes hormones that cause it to develop into an adult (imago) (see HORMONE). While in the pupal stage, the insect develops wings and other structures characteristic of the adult. In many insects, the pupa is enclosed in a covering called a cocoon. The pupa of a butterfly or a moth is often called a chrysalis.
See also BUTTERFLY AND MOTH; CHRYSALIS; COCOON; INSECT.

PURSLANE FAMILY The purslane (pûrs' lĭn) family (Portulacaceae) includes about 500 species

PURSLANE FAMILY
The purslane *Portulaca oleracea* is a weed that multiplies rapidly. Its thick growth soon kills other plants.

of annual and perennial herbaceous plants. They are all dicotyledons (see ANNUAL PLANT; DICOTYLE-DON; HERBACEOUS PLANT; PERENNIAL PLANT). The leaves are simple and fleshy and sometimes form rosettes. The flowers have colorful petals, and many species are grown in gardens.

Members of the genus *Portulaca* are able to withstand unfavorable environmental conditions. They grow in almost any type of soil. The species *Portulaca oleracea* is frequently called pusley or purslane. This weed covers large areas and multiplies very quickly. It covers the ground with such a thick growth that it kills other plants, although one form is grown as a salad vegetable.
See also WEED.

PYRAMID (pĭr'ə mĭd) A pyramid is a large structure with a square base and four triangular-shaped sides that come to a point at the top. In ancient times, people built pyramid-shaped buildings as tombs or temples. The most famous pyramids are those that were built around 4,600 years ago as tombs for Egyptian pharaohs (kings).

The Egyptian pyramids are considered to be among the Seven Wonders of the Ancient World. Ancient pyramids are also found in Mexico and Central and South America.

The ruins of thirty-five pyramids still stand along the Nile River in Egypt. The pyramid of Khufu, called the Great Pyramid, contains more than 2 million stone blocks that average 2.5 tons [2.3 metric tons] each. The pyramid was originally 481 ft. [147 m] tall, but some stones have fallen off, and it is now about 459 ft. [140 m] tall. Its base covers about 13 acres [5 hectares].

The Egyptian pyramids are a miracle of building skill. The ancient Egyptians had no machinery or iron tools. The huge blocks that make up the pyramids were cut out of limestone quarries with copper chisels and saws. They were then dragged many

PYRAMID—Construction

The ancient Egyptians built the pyramids with huge blocks of stone. They had no machinery or iron tools, so they used copper chisels and saws to cut blocks out of limestone quarries. The blocks were then dragged by teams of men across the desert and up ramps to the upper levels of the pyramid.

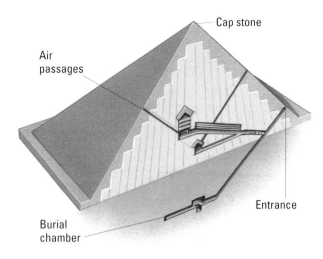

Cap stone

Air passages

Entrance

Burial chamber

PYRAMID—Inside

Deep inside the pyramids are the burial chambers of Egyptian pharaohs. Other rooms held objects the king might need in the next life. After the burial, workmen slid stone blocks down the passages to try to keep out thieves.

miles across the desert by teams of men. More than 400,000 men worked each year for twenty years to build the Great Pyramid. When the first layer of blocks was in place, ramps were built so that blocks could be dragged to upper layers.

Inside the pyramids are hidden chambers that hold the mummified (dried and wrapped in cloth) bodies of Egyptian pharaohs. These rooms were filled with gold and treasure. Passageways connected various other burial chambers inside the pyramid.

The native peoples of Mexico and Central and South America built pyramids that had flat tops. The flat tops served as bases for their temples. The pyramid built by the Toltecs near Cholula, Mexico, is one of the largest pyramids in the world. Other well-known pyramids are located near Mexico City, Mexico, and in Peru.

The pyramid is also a shape in geometry. The base can have three or more sides, and this determines how many triangular side faces there are. A pyramid with three equilateral faces is called a tetrahedron. *See also* GEOMETRY.

PYRITE (pī′rīt′) Pyrite (FeS_2) is a brassy yellow mineral made of iron and sulfur. Because of its color, pyrite is often mistaken for gold. Therefore, it has been given the nickname "fool's gold." Pyrite

can be distinguished from gold by its much higher degree of hardness and brittleness.

Pyrite is an important source of sulfuric acid. Large deposits of pyrite are found in Spain, the United States, Italy, and Norway.
See also GOLD; MINERAL.

PYROMETER (pī rŏm′ĭ tər) A pyrometer is an instrument that is used for measuring high temperatures. Some types of pyrometers measure thermal radiation in any temperature range. It is used, for example, to measure the temperature in a furnace. There are two main kinds of pyrometers: the radiation pyrometer and the optical pyrometer.

In a radiation pyrometer, heat is concentrated by a lens onto a device such as a thermocouple (see THERMOCOUPLE). When a thermocouple is heated, it produces an electrical voltage. The size of the voltage depends on the temperature. Sometimes, a bolometer is used instead of a thermocouple. A bolometer has two strips of platinum. When the platinum strips heat up, the electrical resistance of the strips changes. The change in resistance can be correlated with temperature (see RESISTANCE, ELECTRICAL).

Optical pyrometers use the light coming from a hot object to measure the object's temperature. The brightness and color of the light change with the temperature of the object. The light is compared to the light from a tungsten filament (threadlike structure) (see TUNGSTEN). The filament is seen against the background of light from the object. The voltage through the filament is varied. The changing voltage heats or cools the filament and makes it brighter or dimmer. At a certain voltage, the filament disappears in the background because the color of the object and the color of the tungsten filament are the same. The size of the voltage through the filament can be correlated with the temperature of the object.

PYTHAGOREAN THEOREM (pĭ thăg′ə rē′ən thē′ ər əm) The Pythagorean theorem is a theorem in geometry that states that the square of the length of the hypotenuse of a right triangle equals the sum of the squares of the lengths of the other two sides. A right triangle is a triangle that contains a right angle. The longest side in a right-angled triangle is the one opposite the right angle. This side is called the hypotenuse.

To understand the Pythagorean theorem, consider the following example. Suppose a simple right triangle has sides of 3, 4, and 5 units. The 5-unit side is the hypotenuse. The square of the hypotenuse is 25 (5 x 5). The square of the other sides are 9 (3 x 3) and 16 (4 x 4). By adding those two sides together, we have the equation: 9 + 16 = 25. This shows how the Pythagorean theorem works. People can use the Pythagorean theorem to find the length of one side of a right triangle when the lengths of the other two sides are known.

The Pythagorean theorem is named after the Greek mathematician and philosopher Pythagoras. He lived from about 580 to 500 B.C. However, he probably did not come up with the theorem himself. It is more likely that it was formulated by one of his followers after Pythagoras' death.
See also GEOMETRY.

PYTHON *Python* is a genus that includes 20 to 25 species of large, nonpoisonous snakes belonging to the family Boidae. Pythons are native to the tropical parts of Africa, Asia, and Australia. Most live near the water and are able to swim and climb well. Pythons are related to the boas (see BOA). Unlike the boas, however, pythons are oviparous. This means that they lay eggs that hatch in a nest. A female python lays fifteen to one hundred eggs at a time, depending on her size. She then coils herself around the eggs and incubates them (keeps them warm) for about seventy days. This helps keep the eggs slightly warmer than the surrounding air.

The largest python is the reticulate python. It may reach 31.5 ft. [9.6 m] long and weigh 254 lb. [115 kg]. It rivals the giant anaconda of South America as the world's largest snake. Some reticulate pythons prey on small goats, pigs, and deer, but they usually prefer smaller animals.

The Indian python and the African rock python are smaller, usually less than 23 ft. [7 m] long. They prey on a wide range of animals, including rodents, small antelopes, and birds.

A python kills its prey by wrapping itself in coils around the victim and squeezing it to death. By tightening its coils, the python cuts off a victim's circulation and breathing. The python then swallows the dead victim whole. During the next few days, the python hardly moves at all as it digests its meal.
See also SNAKE.

PYTHON

The Calabar python is a burrowing snake from western Africa. It is one of the smaller species of pythons, growing to a length of only 3.3 ft. [1 m]. When alarmed, the snake curls up with its head on the inside. It then flicks its tail, which resembles the head of a snake that is striking at prey.

Q

QUADRANT The quadrant is an instrument that once was used by navigators at sea for measuring latitude (location north or south of the equator, measured in degrees) (see LATITUDE AND LONGITUDE). Quadrants were also used by astronomers for finding the positions of stars.

A quadrant was made of a strip of metal shaped like a quarter of a circle. Marked on the strip was a scale from 0° to 90°. At each end of the strip there were two more strips of metal. They were joined to each other where the middle of the circle would be. At this joint, a lead weight hung from the end of a cord or another strip of metal. Along one side of the quadrant there were two holes. The navigator would line up these two holes with the pole star (the star toward which the northern end of the earth's axis very nearly points). Someone else would read aloud where the weighted cord passed across the scale. This gave the angle of the pole star above the horizon. This angle was the same as the latitude at that point.

See also NAVIGATION.

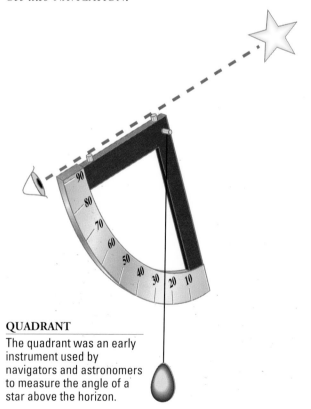

QUADRANT

The quadrant was an early instrument used by navigators and astronomers to measure the angle of a star above the horizon.

QUAIL A quail is a small, chunky, chickenlike bird that belongs to the family Phasianidae. It is closely related to the partridge and pheasant. There are six species of quail in North America. They grow from 7 to 10 in. [17.5 to 25 cm] long. The feathers of the quail are mostly brown, black, and gray in color. The quail's beak is short and stubby. It is used to pick seeds, berries, and insects off the ground. Quails live in fields and other open country. They are popular game birds. One well-known quail is the bobwhite; its name sounds like its call.

QUAIL

The common quail (left) and the bobwhite (right) are two of the six species of North American quail.

QUANTA *Quanta* is the plural of *quantum*, which is a very small quantity into which many forms of energy are subdivided. The word *quanta* was first used by the German physicist Max Planck in 1900 (see PLANCK, MAX). In order to explain a certain property of light, he regarded it as consisting of "packets," or units of energy called quanta.

Today, the word is commonly used in nuclear and particle physics and has a wider meaning. Any quantity that can have only certain values is said to be quantized, or made up of quanta. For example, there exist many different tiny particles called subatomic particles. A subatomic particle is a particle that is smaller than an atom, such as a proton, neutron, or electron (see ATOM). Some subatomic particles spin rather in the same way as a ball spins when it is thrown. The spin can be $1/2$ a unit, or 1, $1^1/2$, 2, and so on. However, it cannot be $2/3$ or $1/4$ of a unit. The spin is said to be quantized, because only these certain spin units, or quanta, are possible. *See also* NUCLEAR PHYSICS; PARTICLE PHYSICS.

QUANTUM THEORY

Quantum theory is a theory in physics based on the general idea that certain kinds of energy are subdivided into quanta (see QUANTA). Quantum mechanics is the application of this theory to such processes as the transference or transformation of energy on an atomic or molecular scale.

At the end of the 1800s, physicists considered light as a wave motion. This theory of light explained almost all of its properties. However, there were some effects that could not be explained. One of these effects was that hot objects give off visible light. For example, a red-hot object gives off mostly red light. The frequency (rate of occurrence) of the light given off depends only on the temperature. The frequency does not depend on the substance out of which the object is made. The wave theory of light tried to explain how the frequency depends on the temperature. However, the theory failed at the frequencies of ultraviolet rays (see ULTRAVIOLET RAY). This failure was known as the ultraviolet catastrophe.

The problem was solved in 1900 by a German physicist, Max Planck (see PLANCK, MAX). He suggested that the light can be thought of as consisting of "packets" of energy. He called these packets of light energy quanta (plural of *quantum*). His theory, which became known as the quantum theory, explained exactly how the frequency changes with the temperature. In Max Planck's theory, the energy of each quantum is proportional to its frequency. This can be written as $E = hf$. Here, E is the energy, f is the frequency, and h is a constant. It is called Planck's constant and is very small indeed. It is equal to 6.6256×10^{-34} joule seconds.

In 1905, the quantum theory solved another problem. When light falls on certain substances, the substances sometimes give off electrons from their atoms. This is called the photoelectric effect (see PHOTOELECTRIC EFFECT). The light has to be above a certain frequency. The wave theory could not explain why light had to be above a certain frequency. However, this was explained in 1905 by the German-American physicist Albert Einstein. He explained it by using Planck's quantum theory (see EINSTEIN, ALBERT). He said that light consisted of particles called photons (see PHOTON).

The next step in the development of the quantum theory came in 1913. In that year, the Danish physicist Niels Bohr used the quantum theory to produce a fairly accurate model of the atom (see ATOM; BOHR, NIELS).

Now, physicists did not know whether light was made up of waves or particles. The wave theory was still needed to explain effects such as the diffraction of light (see DIFFRACTION). However, in certain experiments, light certainly behaved as if it were made up of particles. The situation became even more complicated in 1924. In that year a French physicist, Louis de Broglie, suggested that the parts of the atom known as electrons could behave like

QUANTUM THEORY

The development of the quantum theory in the early 1900s allowed scientists to understand that electrons could, under some circumstances, behave like waves. This understanding made possible the development of the electron microscope (right).

waves. Before this, electrons were thought of as particles (see ELECTRON). Two years later, a new theory of the atom was produced by a German physicist Erwin Schrödinger (see SCHRÖDINGER, ERWIN). His theory was based on de Broglie's idea. Calling his theory wave mechanics, Schrödinger developed an equation for describing the wave properties of electrons. Solutions of this equation were described by four values, known as quantum numbers. These numbers helped physicists describe the energy state of an electron. In 1925, using quantum numbers, the Austrian physicist Wolfgang Pauli developed a principle for determining how electrons are arranged in layers called shells in the atom (see PAULI, WOLFGANG).

At the same time that Schrödinger introduced his theory, another German physicist, Werner Heisenberg, produced a different theory, using mathematical devices called matrices (plural of *matrix*) (see MATRIX). His theory was called matrix mechanics. Later, Schrödinger succeeded in showing that wave mechanics and matrix mechanics are different mathematical approaches to the same theory. Finally, Heisenberg's uncertainty principle helped show that waves and particles are complementary properties of electromagnetic radiation (see ELECTROMAGNETIC RADIATION; UNCERTAINTY PRINCIPLE). Thus, particles can behave like waves under the right conditions. For example, photons and electrons can collide with other particles. A wave could never take part in a collision. However, photons and electrons cannot behave like waves and particles at the same time. They always behave like one or the other.

Since the 1920s, the quantum theory has enabled physicists to understand many aspects of the atomic world. For example, magnetism is now fairly well understood. This would not have been possible without quantum theory (see MAGNETISM). Quantum theory is also used in solid-state physics. Solid-state physics is the branch of physics that studies solids (see SOLID-STATE PHYSICS). Quantum theory explains the properties of solids in terms of the arrangement of their atoms. Quantum theory has enabled physicists to understand how transistors work (see TRANSISTOR). Quantum theory is also an important tool for understanding the subatomic world—that is, the world of particles that are smaller than atoms. With quantum theory, physicists now understand many properties of the atomic nucleus and of radioactivity.

See also NUCLEUS; RADIOACTIVITY.

QUARK A quark is a tiny particle that is believed to make up certain other subatomic particles. A subatomic particle is a particle that is smaller than an atom (see ATOM). Atoms have a central core, called a nucleus (see NUCLEUS). The nucleus is surrounded by electrons (see ELECTRON). The basic structure of atoms was discovered in the early l900s. Scientists later discovered that the nucleus is made of smaller particles called protons and neutrons (see NEUTRON; PROTON). By the early 1960s, scientists had discovered hundreds of other, smaller subatomic particles. These various particles make up larger subatomic particles or are involved in the forces that affect particles.

In 1964, two American physicists, Murray Gell-Mann and George Zweig of the California Institute of Technology, proposed a new theory about subatomic particles. They said certain particles are made up of smaller particles, which they called quarks. By 1971, physicists observed quarks in protons and neutrons using particle accelerators (see ACCELERATORS, PARTICLE).

Different combinations of quarks are believed to make up the subatomic particles called hadrons. Protons, mesons, and neutrons are examples of hadrons (see MESON; PARTICLE PHYSICS). Protons and neutrons are each made of three quarks, while mesons consist of a quark and an antiquark (see MESON).

At first, physicists believed there were three types, called flavors, of quarks. The flavors were named *up (u)*, *down (d)*, and *strange (s)*. However, physicists now believe six quarks exist. The other three quarks are known by the names *charm (c)*, *top (t)*, and *bottom (b)*. *Top* is sometimes called *truth* and *bottom* is sometimes called *beauty*.

Each quark has an antiquark. An antiquark is an antiparticle. Antiparticles are mirror images of their corresponding particles. They may have an opposite electric charge or an opposite direction of spin. *See also* ANTIMATTER; ELEMENTARY PARTICLES.

QUARRYING Quarrying is a process by which stone is taken out of the ground. The excavation, or pit, from which the stone is taken is called a quarry. The type of stone and the way it is to be used determine the method of quarrying.

Granite is difficult to quarry because of its hardness (see GRANITE). Granite is usually quarried by the plug-and-feather method. In this process, a series of small holes are drilled into the rock (see DRILLING). Then, two semicircular pieces of steel, called feathers, are put in each hole. A steel wedge called a plug is forced between the feathers. The plugs and feathers are then driven into the ground, splitting the rock. Further splitting of the rock can often be done by using smaller tools.

Very sophisticated methods are used to quarry marble (see MARBLE). First, a sample of marble is obtained by a machine that drills a deep hole into the deposit. A cylinder of material is taken out, and from it, experts can decide how deep below the surface the best marble is. Grooves are then cut in lines at right angles to each other, forming blocks. The blocks are loosened and taken out by drilling or by the plug-and-feather method.

Stratified (layered) rock is fairly easy to quarry.

Sandstone, slate, and limestone are often quarried by simple drilling or prying. Weak explosives are often used. Stronger explosives are used when broken stone is required for road building.

Stone is quarried throughout the world. Some six thousand quarries in the United States produce 1 billion tons [610 million metric tons] of stone a year.
See also EXCAVATION; MINING.

QUARTZ Quartz is a hard, glossy mineral made of silicon and oxygen. Its chemical formula is SiO_2 (silicon dioxide, or silica) (see SILICA). Quartz breaks much like glass and is common in almost all types of rock.

Pure quartz, called rock crystal, is made entirely of silicon and oxygen. It has a transparent, glassy appearance and is used mainly for jewelry. Impure quartz crystals include amethyst, a purple-colored quartz, and citrine, a golden yellow variety. Noncrystalline quartz, including jasper and flint, is made of many fine grains instead of large single crystals (see CRYSTAL).

Quartz has many electronic uses because of its piezoelectric nature (see PIEZOELECTRIC EFFECT). This property of quartz allows the generation of electric voltage across the crystal when it is deformed. Because of this effect, electrical signals can be changed into sound waves, and vice versa.

QUARRYING
The Colonnata Quarry at Carrara, Italy (left), is famed as a source of fine marble. The sixteenth-century Italian sculptor Michelangelo used Carrara marble to carve many of his statues.

QUARTZ

Quartz, normally transparent, may be colored by impurities. Pure quartz is called rock crystal. It is used for making jewelry.

The piezoelectric effect of quartz plays an important role in radios, television, and radar.

Quartz has many other important uses. It is used to make glass and lenses that transmit ultraviolet rays. It is also used as an abrasive in sandpaper. *See also* MINERAL; ROCK.

QUARTZITE Quartzite is a rock made of quartz crystals (which are made of silica) cemented together by silica (see CRYSTAL; QUARTZ). When split, the quartz crystals as well as the cement split, giving two smooth surfaces.

Quartzite is formed from sandstone in which the quartz crystals have recrystallized. This recrystallization can be caused by heat and pressure, resulting in a kind of quartzite called metaquartzite (see METAMORPHIC ROCK; ROCK; SANDSTONE). Recrystallization can also be caused by silica-laden water, producing a quartzite called orthoquartzite. *See also* SEDIMENTARY ROCK.

QUASAR (kwā'zär') Quasars are very bright heavenly bodies that may be single stars or very young galaxies (see GALAXY; STAR). Quasars were discovered in 1960. Radio astronomers noticed very strong radio signals coming from certain parts of the universe. The astronomers measured the positions of the radio signals in the sky. Then astronomers looked at photographs of those parts of the sky and saw what seemed to be faint blue stars (see RADIO ASTRONOMY).

It is believed that the universe is expanding, because all the distant stars and galaxies seem to be moving away from us. The farther away the stars and galaxies are, the faster they are traveling. Quasars seem to be moving very fast indeed. Therefore, some astronomers think they must be very far away. However, if quasars are very far away, then they must be giving out huge amounts of energy. Otherwise, astronomers would not be able to detect them. The energy that quasars give out is hundreds of times more than the energy that our galaxy produces. There is another strange fact about quasars. Their energy varies over a few weeks or months. This could happen only if they were at

QUARTZITE

Massive outcrops of quartzite rock are dominant features of the Rustenburg Nature Reserve in Transvaal, South Africa.

least a million times smaller than our own galaxy.

It may be that quasars are not as far away as some astronomers think. Some quasars seem to be associated with certain galaxies. Astronomers know that these galaxies are not as far away as the quasars seem to be. If this were true, the quasars' brightness would not be so unusual.

QUATERNARY PERIOD (kwŏt′ər nĕr′ē pĭr′ē əd) The Quaternary period in the earth's history began about 1.64 million years ago and extends to the present. It is divided into the Pleistocene epoch and the Holocene epoch (see GEOLOGICAL TIME SCALE).

During the Quaternary, modern humans emerged (see HUMAN BEING). They domesticated animals and cultivated plants. The later part of the Quaternary saw the extinction of many large mammals. The modern species adapted to their respective ecosystems (see ECOSYSTEM; EXTINCTION).

The major climatic event of the Quaternary was the ice age of the Pleistocene epoch. During the ice age, periods of glaciation shaped the landscape of the world's northern regions. Some geologists believe that the Holocene epoch is actually an interglacial age—that is, a period between glaciers. *See also* ICE AGE; PLEISTOCENE EPOCH.

QUICKSAND Quicksand is a fine, powdery sand saturated (soaked) with water. It is found on the bottoms of brooks and streams and along the seashore.

Quicksand cannot hold very much weight. A person may drown while trying to walk on thick quicksand. It is rare for someone to be swallowed up by quicksand, but a trapped person easily falls face down and drowns in the water covering it. Instead of struggling, a person who falls into quicksand should try to float on top of it by lying flat on the back with the arms stretched out at right angles to the body.

QUININE (kwī′nīn′) Quinine is a bitter substance that is taken from the bark of the cinchona tree. Cinchona trees grow mainly in South America, India, and Indonesia.

Quinine is used mainly in treating diseases, especially malaria. Quinine is especially used in tropical regions where it is easy to obtain and inexpensive. In the United States, quinine has largely been replaced by synthetic (human-made) drugs. However, doctors still use the drug quinidine to treat certain disorders of heart rhythm. Quinidine has the same chemical formula as quinine but differs from it in the way the atoms are arranged in the molecule (see MOLECULE).

Quinine and quinidine may cause abnormalities in unborn children. Pregnant women, therefore, should not take these drugs without first checking with a doctor.
See also MALARIA.

QUININE

The evergreen cinchona tree has glossy green leaves (top). The bark (bottom), sometimes called Peruvian bark, is the source of the drug quinine, which is used to treat malaria.

R

RABBIT Rabbits are small, furry mammals that, along with hares, belong to the family Leporidae (see HARE; MAMMAL). Wild rabbits are usually brown or gray. They are up to 20 in. [50 cm] long and weigh up to 5.5 lb. [2.5 kg]. Pet rabbits may be any of several colors. They are often much larger and heavier than wild rabbits. One breed, known as the Flemish Giant, regularly weighs as much as 20 lb. [9 kg]. Rabbits have small, furry tails. They have a keen sense of smell and are able to move their ears to "catch" even faint sounds.

Rabbits usually live in underground tunnels

RABBIT

There are about forty-four different species of rabbits and hares in the world, including (1) the volcano rabbit from Mexico, (2) the eastern cottontail of North America, (3) the common European rabbit, and (4) the Bunyoro rabbit of central and eastern Africa.

called burrows or in shallow holes called forms. Frequently, these burrows and forms have been dug and abandoned by other animals. Although rabbits commonly live alone, they may form communities and live in warrens. A warren is a group of burrows that have been dug close together. Each warren is ruled by a dominant buck (male) (see DOMINANCE).

Rabbits are peaceful, nonaggressive animals. If threatened, a rabbit may try to hide by staying perfectly still. A frightened rabbit can hop farther than 10 ft. [3 m] in one hop. It can move faster than 18 m.p.h. [30 kph]. A rabbit tires easily, however, and may try to outwit an enemy by running in a circular or zigzag pattern.

Rabbits usually sleep during the day and eat and play at night (see NOCTURNAL BEHAVIOR). They are herbivores and eat almost any kind of plant. Some rabbits cause extensive damage to crops or garden plants and are considered pests.

After mating and a pregnancy of about a month, a female rabbit gives birth to a litter of two to nine babies, called kits. Some rabbits have more than five litters a year. The mother stays near her kits and feeds them for about two weeks. The kits are blind and have almost no hair at birth, and the mother covers them with grass and with fur from her own chest. After two weeks, the kits start to leave the burrow to explore their surroundings.

The two major kinds of rabbits are the cottontails, or New World rabbits (genus *Sylvilagus*), and the European rabbits, or Old World rabbits (genus *Oryctolagus*). Cottontails live in North and South America, from Canada to Argentina and Paraguay. European rabbits are native to Europe and northern Africa. They have since been introduced into many other countries, including Australia, where they have caused immense damage to the grazing lands and forests. Some of the natural enemies of rabbits include birds of prey, cats, dogs, coyotes, foxes, minks, weasels, and wolves. Human beings, however, are the greatest enemies of rabbits. They hunt rabbits for their skin, fur, and meat. In areas where they are pests, rabbits are poisoned or trapped in great numbers.

See also BIOLOGICAL CONTROL.

RABIES (rā'bēz) Rabies is a disease that is caused by a virus. The disease, which almost always causes death if untreated, destroys the nerve cells of part of the brain. The infection is caused by a virus that lives in the saliva of a carrier (called a host). Most mammals can carry the virus. If the host bites a human being or other animal, the victim may get rabies. The virus can also enter mucous membranes (such as the lining of the nose), but it cannot enter unbroken skin.

In human beings, symptoms of rabies include pain, a burning feeling, or numbness where the infection occurred; restlessness; fever; headache; and, possibly, seizures, highly disturbed (maniacal) behavior, or paralysis. Another symptom is difficulty in swallowing. Because of this, rabies is also called *hydrophobia,* which means "fear of water." Sometimes the mere sight of water creates painful throat contractions. After a day or two, a quiet period occurs, followed by unconsciousness and death. The disease lasts from three to twelve days.

Most animals infected with rabies wander around restlessly, make sounds constantly, and will attack without reason. Paralysis of the jaw and throat are followed by general paralysis and death. Some infected animals only show signs of paralysis, called "dumb rabies."

Any person bitten by an animal should wash the wound immediately with soap and water and see a doctor. The animal should be penned and watched to see if it shows any symptoms of rabies. If such symptoms occur, the person who was bitten should be treated at once. Generally, patients receive a one-time dose of antibodies that neutralize the virus before it causes disease (see ANTIBODY; SERUM). In addition, a vaccine is given by injection in five separate doses over a month's time (see VACCINATION). Each year in the United States, approximately twenty thousand people receive this treatment, and there are six or fewer actual cases of human rabies. *See also* PASTEUR, LOUIS.

RACCOON The raccoon is a furry mammal belonging to the same family of carnivores as lesser pandas, kinkajous, and ringtails (see CARNIVORE; MAMMAL). Raccoons are found in much of North America and in the northern half of South America.

The raccoon is usually gray in color, sometimes tinged with yellow or brown. It has a bushy ringed tail and is especially noted for a band of black hair around its eyes that resembles a mask. Raccoons have pointed snouts and strong, sharp claws. The animals use their paws to find food. They can handle objects very skillfully.

There are two main species of raccoons. The northern raccoon lives in Canada, the United States, and Central America. It measures from 30 to 38 in. [76 to 97 cm] in length, including the tail. Males are generally larger than females. The crab-eating raccoon lives in South America. This raccoon has shorter hair and longer legs than the northern raccoon.

Raccoons live both on the ground and in trees. They may live alone or in small family groups. Each raccoon has a home range. Within this range, which may cover 200 acres [81 hectares], the raccoon mates, builds its home, and searches for food. Raccoons usually hunt for food at night. They eat a variety of foods, such as crabs, crayfish, frogs, fish, acorns, corn, fruit, grasshoppers, and mice.

Northern raccoons mate once a year between January and June. About nine weeks after mating, the female has from one to seven babies.

RACCOON
The northern raccoon, common throughout North and Central America, often hunts for food in garbage cans.

RADAR

Radar (rā′där) is a method of detecting and locating objects using radio waves (see RADIO). It can be used to find objects as small as insects or as large as mountains. The word *radar* stands for "*ra*dio *d*etection *a*nd *r*anging." Radar works on the same principle that bats use when they fly at night. As a bat flies, it sends out very high frequency sounds in short bursts. The sounds are too high-pitched for human beings to hear. The sounds bounce off objects and are reflected (bounced) back. The bat can hear the reflections and determine the direction and distance of the objects (see BAT).

In radar, radio waves rather than sound waves are used. There are two main types of radar: pulsed radar and continuous radar. Pulsed radar is the most common and sends out short pulses of radio waves. If an object is in the path of the waves, it reflects the waves back toward the radar equipment. The reflected wave is called the echo (see ECHO). The time taken for the echo to be picked up by the radar equipment depends on the distance of the object. The farther away an object is, the longer it takes for the radio wave to be returned. From this, an exact distance can be figured. Most radar equipment has a screen on which echoes appear as bright spots. A scale marked on the screen shows the direction and distance of the object.

The uses of radar Radar was first developed in the late 1930s and 1940s for use in air defense during World War II (1939–1945). Today, radar is widely used in air and sea navigation (see NAVIGATION). It is especially useful in locating and guiding airplanes and ships at night or in fog. Radar is also used to help aircraft and ships avoid collisions and help them land and dock safely. One airplane may have several kinds of radar. For example, one kind may show how high the airplane is flying. Another kind may detect storms. The pilot may then decide to change his or her course to avoid the storm.

Radar is used in military defense to warn of attack by air weapons, such as missiles (see MISSILE). Very powerful radar equipment is used to track orbiting spacecraft and to help them land safely when they return to Earth. Radar equipment also can be used on the spacecraft itself. For example, spacecraft use radar to help map the surfaces of other planets.

Radar is used by weather forecasters to track weather systems, such as hurricanes. Radar has the ability to tell the difference between the small raindrops produced by an ordinary cloud and hailstones produced in a thunderstorm. Scientists use radar to track the migration of birds. Police officers monitor driving speeds using radar. Portable continuous wave radar sets in police cars detect the distance, direction, and speed of a vehicle. These radar sets operate by sending out a continuous signal, unlike the pulses sent out by most other radar methods. The vehicle is tracked using the Doppler effect (see DOPPLER EFFECT). The speed of pitches in professional baseball games is often measured

AIRPORT RADAR

Radar equipment on a tall tower is a familiar sight at airports. The radar tracks the movements of aircraft approaching and leaving the airport.

integrated circuits or transistors (see INTEGRATED CIRCUIT; TRANSISTOR).

Surrounding the antenna is a device called a reflector. The reflector may be shaped like a dish, funnel, or trough. The microwaves being sent from the antenna bounce off the reflector and are focused in a particular direction. The antenna and reflector are mounted on a platform called a scanner. The scanner rotates, usually ten to twenty-five times a minute. The rotating scanner allows the radio waves to be sent out in all directions. A device called a phase shifter allowed the development of a type of radar called phased array radar. In a phased array system, the signal moves out into the air electronically rather than through the mechanical rotating of an antenna. Phased array radars can send out signals very rapidly. They are often used as a way to detect missiles.

If the radio waves that are sent out hit an object, some of them will be reflected back to the radar set. An instrument called a receiver picks up the radio waves. The receiver amplifies the radio waves, which have become weaker because of traveling long distances. The receiver also converts the microwaves back into an electronic signal. The electronic signal is fed into a cathode-ray tube (see CATHODE-RAY TUBE). The signal appears as a bright spot on the screen of the cathode-ray tube. The screen is called an indicator. The most common type of indicator is the plan position indicator (PPI). The indicator has a line radiating from the middle of the screen to the outer edge. The line rotates around the screen every time the scanner rotates. A pattern of rings marked on the indicator indicates different distances. The screen also has marks showing the directions of north, south, east, and west. The radar operator can determine the location of the object represented by the bright spot and its distance from the radar set using the pattern of rings and the direction markers.

Since the late 1960s, optical, or laser, radar has come into use. Optical radar sends out short beams of light rather than microwaves (see LASER). Optical radar is often used to precisely determine short distances between objects.

INDICATOR EQUIPMENT
Many radar sets have a television-type display. Called a plan position indicator (PPI), it shows the positions of objects—such as airplanes or ships—within the range of the radar.

using a hand-held radar set that also sends a continuous signal.

How radar works Most radar sets contain several devices. The modulator switches another device, called a transmitter, on and off. This causes the transmitter to send out short pulsed signals. The transmitter may contain a vacuum tube called a magnetron (see VACUUM TUBE). When an electric signal passes through the magnetron, the magnetron gives out very short radio waves, called microwaves (see MICROWAVE). A more powerful vacuum tube, called a klystron, is sometimes used to produce microwaves. A klystron amplifies (strengthens) the microwaves it gives out.

The radio waves are then fed into an aerial (see ANTENNA). The aerial transmits the microwaves through the air. Since the 1960s, many radar sets have replaced the magnetron and klystron with

RADIATION (rā′dē ā′shən) Radiation is a flow of particles or waves from a source. Light, X rays, and radio waves are forms of radiation (see ELECTROMAGNETIC RADIATION). Another example is the radiation given off by radioactive substances (see RADIOACTIVITY). Three of the more common kinds of radiation that can be given off are alpha particles, beta particles, and gamma rays (see ALPHA PARTICLE; BETA PARTICLE; GAMMA RAY). High doses of certain kinds of radiation over short periods of time can be damaging to various organisms, including human beings. However, controlled applications of radiation can be helpful—for example, in treating cancer.

See also RADIATION THERAPY; RADIOGRAPHY; RADIOLOGY. PROJECT 39, 40

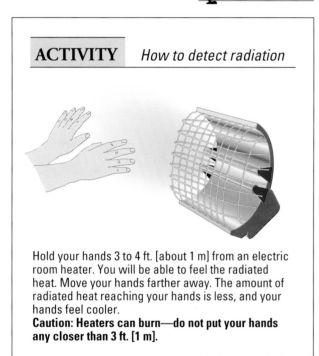

ACTIVITY *How to detect radiation*

Hold your hands 3 to 4 ft. [about 1 m] from an electric room heater. You will be able to feel the radiated heat. Move your hands farther away. The amount of radiated heat reaching your hands is less, and your hands feel cooler.
Caution: Heaters can burn—do not put your hands any closer than 3 ft. [1 m].

RADIATION THERAPY (rā′dē ā′shən thĕr′ə pē) Radiation therapy is the use of radiation to cure disease. It is a branch of radiology (see RADIATION; RADIOLOGY). The radiation used is very high-energy radiation—gamma rays and X rays (see GAMMA RAY; X RAY). These rays are very penetrating. In large doses, the rays are very destructive. They damage and destroy living cells. However, this destructive effect can sometimes be put to good use. By carefully calculating the dosage of radiation, a radiation therapist, also called a radiation

oncologist, can destroy unwanted cells without damaging healthy tissues too much.

Radiation has its greatest effect on cells that are dividing to produce new cells. In cancer, the cells of a tissue grow and divide more than normal. They are "runaway" cells, not controlled by the normal mechanisms that prevent cellular overgrowth. They grow and produce unnatural swellings, or tumors, in different parts of the body. If the rapidly dividing cells are killed, cancer may be slowed down or completely stopped (see CANCER).

To destroy a cancer, a beam of high-energy X rays or gamma rays is focused on it. Alternatively, a beam of high-energy particles such as protons or electrons may be used. The rays are directed from a quantity of radioactive substance or from a machine such as a linear accelerator (see ACCELERATORS, PARTICLE). The particles are produced by machines. Sometimes a radioactive pellet or radioactive needles may be inserted into the tumor. In some cases, a patient may be given an injection of a radioisotope that becomes concentrated in a particular body tissue (see RADIOACTIVITY). Cancer of the thyroid gland may be treated in this way, with radioactive iodine compounds. Cobalt-60 is another radioisotope used in treating some forms of cancer.

See also COBALT.

RADICAL (răd′ĭ kəl) A radical is a group of atoms in a molecule that usually is not affected by a chemical reaction (see CHEMICAL REACTION). An example is the methyl radical (CH_3-). It is found in compounds such as methanol (CH_3OH) and acetaldehyde (CH_3CHO) (see COMPOUND). Another example is the phenyl radical (C_6H_5-). These two radicals are found combined together in the compound toluene ($C_6H_5CH_3$). Usually, radicals are found combined only with other radicals or with atoms in compounds. Sometimes, however, they may be freed from a compound by a chemical reaction. They are then called free radicals and possess an odd number of electrons. Free radicals are very reactive and quickly combine with other radicals or atoms to form a compound.

See also ELEMENT.

Radio is the process of sending invisible electromagnetic waves called radio waves from one place to another (see ELECTROMAGNETIC RADIATION). Radio is one of our most important means of communication. It allows people to send signals, such as codes, music, and words, through the air to any part of the world. Radio is also used to communicate far into space.

Broadcasting is the most familiar form of radio. Radio broadcasts include advertising, discussions, interviews, music, news, and sports events. People wake up to clock radios, ride to work or school listening to automobile or portable radios, and spend leisure hours listening to favorite radio programs.

Radio has many other uses in addition to broadcasting. Airplane pilots, astronauts, construction workers, police officers, taxicab drivers, and many other people use a type of radio called short-wave radio for quick communication. Others, called radio amateurs, operate short-wave radio stations in their homes as a hobby. Citizen's Band radio (CB), another type of radio, became very popular in the 1970s. CB radio is a means of radio communication over short distances. Many car motorists and truck drivers use CB radio to talk with other highway travelers or with people who are in an office or at home. CB radio allows signals to be sent for distances of fewer than 5 mi. [8 km] in city areas and up to 20 mi. [32 km] in rural areas. Walkie-talkies are small, portable two-way radios that may operate on CB frequencies (see FREQUENCY). Cellular telephones permit nationwide person-to-person communication. The telephone handset sends radio signals to transmitters that relay the signals to their destination.

How broadcasting works Broadcasting works by changing sounds that come from a room called a studio into electromagnetic waves. The electromagnetic waves travel over wires to a control board. The control board has many switches and dials. A technician at the control board can alter the sound as desired, varying the volume (loudness) of each sound or even blending sounds together. From the control board, the electromagnetic waves go to a device called the transmitter. The transmitter strengthens the waves representing the broadcast. It also produces other electromagnetic waves, called carrier waves. The carrier waves are combined with the waves from the broadcast to form the radio signal that is transmitted (sent). The transmitter may be located in the same room or building as the control board or at the site of the antenna (see ANTENNA). This is a towerlike device that actually

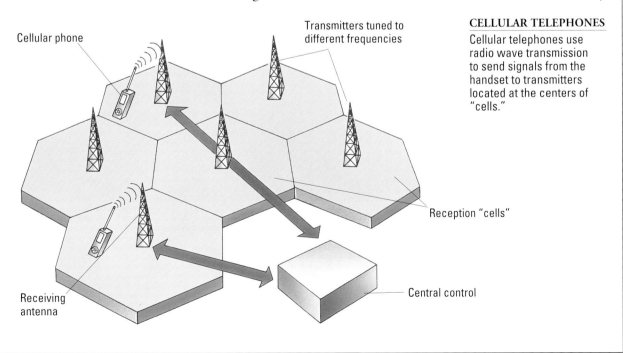

Cellular phone

Transmitters tuned to different frequencies

CELLULAR TELEPHONES
Cellular telephones use radio wave transmission to send signals from the handset to transmitters located at the centers of "cells."

Reception "cells"

Receiving antenna

Central control

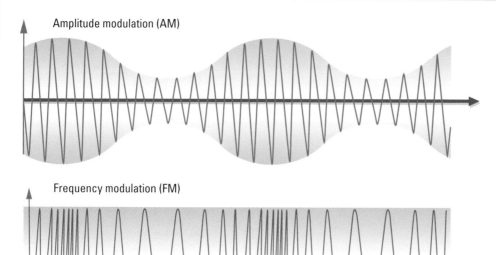

Amplitude modulation (AM)

Frequency modulation (FM)

MODULATION
Information is added to a continuously transmitted radio wave (called a carrier wave) by modulating it. In amplitude modulation (AM), the amplitude of the carrier wave is changed. In frequency modulation (FM), the frequency of the carrier wave is changed.

sends the radio waves out into the air. Antennas are usually located in high or open areas away from buildings that might interfere with the radio waves. Radio waves travel at 186,000 mi. [299,792 km] per second. When the radio waves reach a device called a radio receiver, the receiver changes them back into the original sounds.

Radio waves Radio waves are the longest waves in the electromagnetic spectrum. The shortest radio waves are called microwaves (see MIC-ROWAVE). Microwaves are from 0.04 in. to 12 in. [1 mm to 30 cm] in length. Microwaves are preferred over longer radio waves for many uses, such as sending radio and television broadcast signals, because their signals are of higher quality. They are also used for sending signals between Earth and spacecraft and satellites. Radio waves longer than microwaves are divided into high-frequency and low-frequency ranges. Two types of radio waves in the high-frequency range are used to transmit certain television signals (see TELEVI-SION). Very high-frequency (VHF) waves measure from 3.281 to 32.81 ft. [1 to 10 m]. Ultra high-frequency (UHF) waves measure from 0.3281 to 3.281 ft. [0.1 to 1 m]. Radio astronomers use some of the radio waves that are in the low-frequency range to study the universe (see RADIO ASTRONOMY).

The radio waves used in radio broadcasts, which can be both microwaves and longer radio waves, are transmitted in one of two ways: amplitude modulation (AM) or frequency modulation (FM). In AM transmission, the amplitude (strength) of the carrier waves varies to match changes in the electromagnetic waves coming from the radio studio (see AMPLITUDE). In FM transmission, the amplitude of the carrier waves remains constant. However, the frequency of the waves (the number of times they vibrate each second) changes to match the electromagnetic waves sent from the studio.

The antenna sends out two kinds of AM waves: ground waves and sky waves. Ground waves spread out horizontally from the antenna. They travel through the air along the earth's surface. Sky waves spread up into the sky. When they reach the layer of atmosphere called the ionosphere, they may be reflected back to Earth (see ATMOSPHERE). This reflection enables AM radio waves to be received at great distances from the antenna.

FM radio waves also travel horizontally and sky-ward. However, due to the higher frequency of the carrier waves, the waves that go skyward are not reflected. They pass through the atmosphere and into space. The FM waves that travel horizontally from the antenna do so in what is called line-of-sight transmission. That is, FM waves cannot be

RADIO STUDIO

Radio broadcasts are made from a soundproof studio at the radio station. A window separates the studio from the technicians in the control room.

received farther than they are "seen" by the antenna. Although AM waves can be received at greater distances than FM waves, FM waves do have advantages. They are not affected by static as much as AM waves. Static is caused by electricity in the atmosphere. FM waves also result in a truer reproduction of sound than AM waves.

Another factor that influences the distance a radio program can be heard is the power of the transmitter. Small AM stations operate at about 250 watts and usually serve only one or two towns

(see WATT). The strongest AM stations have a power of 50,000 watts. They can be heard far away. For example, a 50,000-watt station in Chicago can be heard by listeners in Connecticut, which is about 900 mi. [1,440 km] away. The power of FM stations ranges from 100 watts to 100,000 watts. The 100-watt stations can broadcast about 15.5 mi. [25 km]. The 100,000-watt stations can broadcast over 62 mi. [100 km].

Each radio station operates on its own assigned channel, or frequency. This keeps stations from interfering with each other's broadcasts. Stations also have their own call letters, or names, such as WCKG (Chicago), WOR (New York City), WWL (New Orleans), KOOL (Phoenix), and KMPC

(Los Angeles). Frequency is measured in units called kilohertz and megahertz (see HERTZ). One kilohertz equals 1,000 hertz, and one megahertz equals 1 million hertz. AM stations broadcast on frequencies of between 535 and 1,605 kilohertz. The FM band extends from 88 to 108 megahertz.

Radio receivers Radio waves cannot be seen, heard, or felt. Radio receivers pick them up and change them into sounds that make up the broadcast. Some radios can receive only AM signals. Other radios can receive both AM and FM. Some radios, including larger portable radios, can also receive short-wave radio signals and transmissions from aircraft and ships.

Almost all radios operate on electric power either from a wall outlet or a battery. The main parts of a radio are the antenna, or aerial, the tuner, the amplifiers, and the loudspeaker. The antenna is a length of wire or metal rod that picks up the radio waves. It can be entirely inside the radio, or part of it may be attached to the outside of the radio. The tuner is the device that makes it possible to pick out a particular frequency from all the radio waves that strike the antenna. Amplifiers strengthen the signal selected by the tuner through what is called a superheterodyne circuit. The main operating parts of this circuit in modern radios are transistors. Before the mid-1950s, vacuum tubes were used (see TRANSISTOR; VACUUM TUBE). The loudspeaker is the final link in the system. It changes the electromagnetic signals back into the original sounds (see LOUDSPEAKER).

Stereophonic radio receivers pick up stereo broadcasts. A stereo broadcast sends sound signals from two microphones on one radio wave. The stereophonic receiver then has a special decoding device that allows the signals to be distributed through two loudspeakers. Stereophonic radio has helped keep radio a growing and popular industry. In 1961, the U.S. government allowed FM stations to broadcast in stereo. Today, almost all FM stations are stereo. In 1982, AM stations were also allowed to broadcast in stereo. This caused AM/FM stereo radio sales, especially those for automobiles and portable models, to climb. Today, several hundred AM stations in the United States broadcast in stereo.

Radio in the United States There are about 9,700 privately owned commercial radio stations in the United States. There are more than 1,000 stations operated by colleges and universities. There are also more than 1,700 noncommercial radio stations. Sponsors spent over $9 billion in 1993 for radio advertising. A station in a large city may charge as much as $1,500 for a 30-second commercial announcement. A small station may charge as little as $1. About 40 percent of the commercial stations in the United States are affiliated with national networks, such as ABC, CBS, and NBC. A national network is an organization that provides some of the programming for its member stations. The networks also sell some of the stations' advertising time. Americans spent over $300 million in 1993 to buy almost twenty million table, clock, and portable radios. About 99 percent of American households have a radio.

The Federal Communications Commission (FCC) regulates all communication by radio in the United States. It issues licenses to all radio stations and assigns frequencies and call letters. In Canada, the Canadian Broadcasting Corporation (CBC) performs the same function.

History In 1895, Guglielmo Marconi, an Italian inventor, sent the first radio signals through the air (see MARCONI, GUGLIELMO). These signals traveled more than 1 mi. [1.6 km]. By 1901, he was able to send signals across the Atlantic Ocean from England to Newfoundland.

Reginald A. Fessenden, a Canadian-born physicist, broadcast the first human speech in 1906. He spoke from Massachusetts to ships in the Atlantic Ocean. Lee De Forest, an American inventor, produced the first experimental radio show in 1910. It was broadcast from the Metropolitan Opera House in New York City and featured the famous singer, Enrico Caruso (see DE FOREST, LEE). Edwin H. Armstrong, also from the United States, developed

ANIMAL TRACKING
Scientists use radio to track the movements of animals. This loggerhead turtle carries a radio transmitter that sends out signals picked up by a satellite orbiting the earth.

the superheterodyne circuit in 1918. In 1933, he discovered how to make FM broadcasts. The first commercial radio station was WWJ in Detroit. It began regular broadcasts on August 20, 1920. Its broadcast of the results of the presidential election on November 2, 1920, is considered by many people to be the real beginning of American radio broadcasting.

Radio broadcasting today The rise of television in the early 1950s caused many people to speculate that it would completely do away with radio. However, this has not happened. The audience for radio has continued to grow. Rock music, talk shows, call-in shows (by telephone), and increased coverage of professional sports events has helped radio grow. The increased availability of portable and automobile radios also has contributed to the growth. Of the over 580 million radios owned by Americans in 1994, over 370 million are in the home and more than 210 million are outside the home. The newest radio

technology is digital radio. Digital radio has advantages over AM and FM signals. Digital radio reproduces even truer sounds than FM. Also, digital signals are not affected by the static that can often distort AM signals.

In digital radio, the electromagnetic wave is measured by a device called a digital converter. The converter measures the wave 44,100 times a second. Each of these measurements is given a different digital code. These codes are binary, meaning they are zero, one, or a combination of the two numbers (see BINARY NUMBERS). The codes are then "strung together" and combined with the carrier waves. A digital radio receiver has a device called a digital-to-analog converter. This device changes the codes to electric signals.

Many radio stations already have digital transmitting equipment and are broadcasting digital transmissions on an experimental basis. However, because digital receivers are still very expensive to buy, few people are able to listen to these transmissions. When the price of digital receivers comes down, more and more people are likely to listen to digital radio. Digital radio is eventually expected to replace both AM and FM radio.
See also TELECOMMUNICATION.

RADIOACTIVITY

Radioactivity (rā´dē ō ăk´ tĭv´ĭtē) is the property that some elements have of giving off particles or waves. All matter in the universe is made up of particles called atoms (see ATOM; ELEMENT). Atoms have a central core called a nucleus. The nucleus contains two main kinds of particles—protons that have a positive electric charge and neutrons that have no charge. Protons and neutrons are made up of even smaller particles (see PARTICLE PHYSICS). The nucleus is surrounded by tiny particles called electrons. Electrons have a negative electric charge.

The heavier elements have a large number of protons and neutrons in their nuclei. This causes

ROBOT HELP

Many radioactive chemicals give off harmful radiation. By using a pair of robot "hands," this scientist can mix dangerous chemicals from a safe distance.

them to become unstable. An element that is unstable is referred to as a radioactive element. The nuclei of radioactive elements are in a constant process of breaking up, or decaying. As these nuclei decay, they give off radiation (see RADIATION). This radiation can be in the form of alpha particles or beta particles. Radioactive elements can also give off radiation in the form of gamma rays (see ALPHA PARTICLE; BETA PARTICLE; GAMMA RAY).

Alpha particles are positively charged particles that each consist of two protons and two neutrons bound together (see NEUTRON; PROTON). Alpha decay involves the nucleus releasing an alpha particle. Beta particles are electrons (see ELECTRON). Most beta particles are negatively charged electrons. However, some beta particles, called positrons, are positively charged. During beta decay, one of the neutrons in a nucleus may turn into a negatively charged beta particle (electron), a proton, and an antineutrino. An antineutrino is an antiparticle to the kind of particle called a neutrino (see ANTIMATTER; NEUTRINO). The antineutrino and the electron are ejected. However, the proton stays in the nucleus.

In another type of beta decay, one of the protons in a nucleus turns into a negatively charged beta particle (positron), a neutron, and a neutrino. The positron and the neutrino are ejected, while the neutron remains in the nucleus. In both alpha and beta decay, the number of protons and neutrons in the nucleus changes. Whenever the number of protons changes, the nucleus changes into the nucleus of a different element. This process is called transmutation (see TRANSMUTATION OF ELEMENTS). Whenever the number of neutrons changes, the element remains the same. Only now, it is referred to as an isotope (see ISOTOPE).

Gamma rays are not particles as alpha and beta particles are. They are high-energy electromagnetic rays that are similar to X rays (see ELECTROMAGNETIC RADIATION; X RAY). The giving off of gamma rays does not involve a change in the number of neutrons or protons in a nucleus.

Radioactive series Sometimes, a radioactive element decays into another radioactive element. This new radioactive element then may decay into yet another radioactive element. Eventually, a stable element is formed. This series of transformations is called a radioactive series.

In nature, three main radioactive series occur. Two of these begin with isotopes of uranium—uranium-235 and uranium-238 (see URANIUM). The third series starts with thorium-232. At each stage in the series, the element decays. It gives off either an alpha particle or a beta particle and gamma rays. For example, thorium-232 gives off an alpha particle. In doing so, it reduces its relative atomic mass by four. Relative atomic mass is the number of protons and neutrons in an element (see RELATIVE ATOMIC MASS). Thorium-232 has become a new element, radium-228. Its radioactive series is a complex process that continues until the atoms form lead, the heaviest stable element.

Scientists measure the point at which half the mass of a radioactive substance decays. This length of time is referred to as the half-life (see HALF-LIFE).

For example, the half-life of radium-226 is 1,620 years. The half-lives of other substances may be a fraction of a second or millions of years.

Radioisotopes Some isotopes, called radioisotopes, are radioactive. Some radioisotopes occur naturally. Others are made in large machines called particle accelerators (see ACCELERATORS, PARTICLE). A common method of producing artificial radioisotopes is to bombard an isotope with neutrons. Some of the neutrons may be absorbed into the nuclei of the isotope, changing the number of neutrons.

Radioisotopes have many different uses. For example, knowledge of the half-lives of natural radioisotopes of the metals potassium and uranium is used to figure the age of rocks. Carbon 14 is used in a similar way to determine the age of bone and wood. This is called radiocarbon dating (see DATING).

Radioisotopes also can be used in medicine for treatment and diagnosis. For example, radiation from cobalt-60 is used to destroy cancer growths (see RADIATION THERAPY). Small amounts of a radioactive substance can be placed in a patient's food or injected into the patient. The substance is attracted to a particular area of the patient's body. A specially trained physician then uses a device called a scintillation camera that senses the substance in the body. The camera records this information on a display screen or film (see NUCLEAR MEDICINE).

Other radioactive substances can be used in industry. For example, gamma rays are used to find cracks in metal structures. In factories, beta particles are sometimes passed above a long sheet of material being produced. Detectors measure the amount of beta particles coming through the sheet. A decrease in the number of beta particles at a particular point means the sheet has thickened at that point. Certain adjustments may then be made so that the sheet continues to be produced at the desired thickness.

Dangers of radioactive substances The radiation given off by a radioactive substance can be very dangerous to life. For example, nuclear

NUCLEAR WASTE
One of the problems facing nuclear industry is what to do with radioactive waste. These underground storage tanks (left) are being constructed at Hanford, Washington. Each of the tanks will be able to hold a million gallons [3.8 million liters] of liquid waste.

RADIOACTIVE DECAY
Uranium-238 is the starting material in one of the three natural radioactive decay series (right). This series involves fourteen different radioactive isotopes before finally forming lead-206, which is not radioactive. The radiation given off at each stage in the chain involves alpha particles or beta particles, often accompanied by gamma rays.

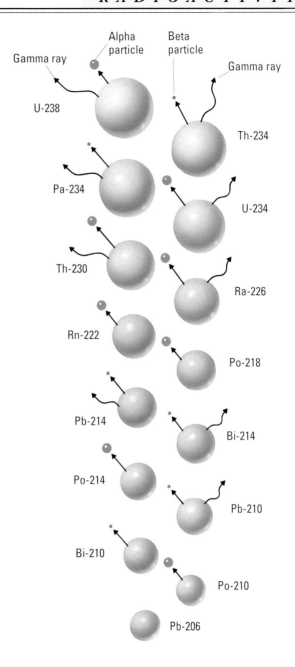

Gamma ray
Alpha particle
Beta particle
Gamma ray
U-238
Th-234
Pa-234
U-234
Th-230
Ra-226
Rn-222
Po-218
Pb-214
Bi-214
Po-214
Pb-210
Bi-210
Po-210
Pb-206

weapons release large amounts of radiation that can kill or injure large numbers of people (see NUCLEAR WEAPONS). Many precautions are taken when radioactive substances are used in medicine and industry. Sometimes, radioactive substances are handled by mechanical devices, which are operated by remote control (see REMOTE CONTROL). Workers have to be shielded from radiation by thick lead or concrete walls. These walls must be thick enough to absorb the radiation.

Radiation is produced in nuclear power plants (see NUCLEAR ENERGY). Certain problems result from this. First, nuclear energy produces radioactive wastes (see WASTE DISPOSAL). Over 18,000 tons [16,300 metric tons] of radioactive wastes have been produced in the United States. Disposal of these wastes has become a serious problem. At present, the waste is put into radiation-proof containers. These containers are then stored at the nuclear power plant. In addition, the machinery and buildings of a nuclear power plant eventually become saturated with radiation and must be abandoned after about twenty years of operation. Also, any accidental leakage of radioactive materials from nuclear reactors is highly dangerous to living things.

See also CHERNOBYL.

RADIO ASTRONOMY

Radio astronomy is the branch of astronomy that uses radio waves to investigate the universe. Reflecting and refracting telescopes—both called optical telescopes—are used to detect light waves given out by heavenly bodies. Radio telescopes are used to detect radio waves coming from outer space (see ASTRONOMY; TELESCOPE). Radio waves are produced by stars, including our sun; planets; and gas clouds. Radio waves have a much longer wavelength than visible light (see FREQUENCY). For this reason, radio telescopes need to be much larger than optical telescopes, so that they can bring radio waves into sharp focus.

Radio waves are picked up by the part of the telescope called the antenna (see ANTENNA). The antenna is tuned to pick up radio waves of a particular wavelength. In this, it is similar to an ordinary radio that is tuned to a particular station. Many radio telescopes have just one antenna. Others have two that are spaced some distance apart. Both antennas are pointed at the same source of radio waves. The signals they receive are combined. This results in interference, which tells the astronomer more about the source than just one antenna would (see INTERFERENCE; INTERFEROMETER).

Radio telescopes may have several antennas. They may be arranged in a circle or in a cross. They allow the telescope to pick up even more details about the source. Bigger radio telescopes have lines of antennas that may stretch for several miles.

Radio telescopes are used not only for picking up signals. They can also be used like a radar set. They can beam radio waves at the moon or at a planet and detect the signal that is reflected, or turned back. Using this method, radio astronomers can map heavenly bodies through thick clouds that may surround them and prevent light from passing through.

Radio astronomy began in 1931. In that year, an American radio engineer, Karl Jansky, was investigating interference in radios. He found that faint radio noises were coming from the center of our galaxy. Six years later, the first radio telescope was built by an American amateur radio operator, Grote Reber. Then, during World War II (1939–1945), radar was developed. Radar also uses radio waves (see RADAR). The knowledge gained in developing radar was applied to radio astronomy.

The first giant radio telescope was built in 1957. It is at the Jodrell Bank Observatory in Manchester, England. lts dish-shaped reflector (which collects the radio waves and focuses them on the antenna) has a diameter of 250 ft. [76 m]. In the 1960s, American scientists built a larger radio telescope in a mountain hollow in Puerto Rico. Its reflector is l,000 ft. [305 m] across. A similar telescope with a reflector 2,000 ft. [610 m] in diameter has been built in Russia. The world's most powerful radio telescope is in New Mexico. It has twenty-seven reflectors, each measuring 82 ft. [25 m] in diameter.

Radio astronomers have made a number of

important discoveries. For instance, pulsars and quasars both give out radio waves. They were first detected by radio telescopes in the 1960s (see PULSAR; QUASAR). Radio astronomy has been used to study the planets as well. Measurements have been made of their temperatures, distances from other heavenly bodies, and the conditions of their surfaces.

Hydrogen gas gives out radiation with various wavelengths. One type of radiation is a radio wave with a wavelength of 8.3 in. [21 cm] (see RADIATION). Radio astronomers can tune into this wavelength. This has allowed them to discover the shape of our galaxy. It has a central core of stars with several curved arms leading out. A number

of other galaxies also have this shape (see GALAXY).

In 1965, radio astronomers discovered that there is a faint background radiation throughout the universe. According to the big bang theory of how the universe formed, the universe exploded into being about 7 to 20 billion years ago (see BIG BANG THEORY). Most astronomers now think that the background radiation is heat left over from that explosion.

See also ASTROPHYSICS; OBSERVATORY.

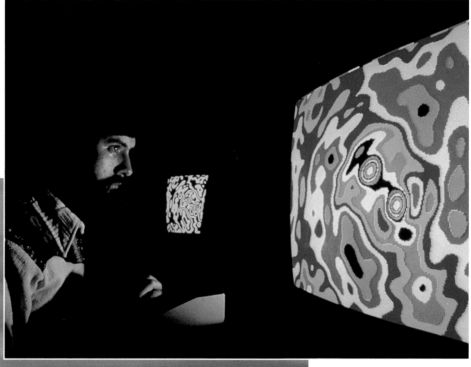

COMPUTER IMAGE

Radio astronomers use sophisticated electronic equipment to study radio waves that reach the earth from space. This astronomer (above) is studying an image created by a computer. The image shows different wavelengths, picked up by a radio telescope, as different colors.

RADIO ARRAY

A number of radio telescopes—some mounted on a railed track so that they can be moved—is called an array (left). The group of small telescopes acts like one huge telescope, and it can pick up very faint radio signals from outer space.

RADIO CONTROL Radio control is a method of controlling machines from a distance by using radio signals. A common example is radio-controlled model aircraft and boats. The model contains a small instrument that picks up radio signals. It is called the receiver. The operator is some distance away and has a transmitter. The transmitter sends radio signals to the receiver in the model. When the receiver picks up a signal, an electric current is produced in it. This current then operates one of the controls in the model. The signals can carry a number of different commands for the controls.

Radio control is also used to guide probes in space exploration, missiles, and satellites. Unmanned aircraft called drones also can be guided by radio signals.

RADIO CONTROL

A stretch of flat, sandy desert makes an ideal place for flying a radio-controlled model aircraft.

RADIOGRAPHY Radiography is the use of radiation to make hidden structures visible. Radiologists—physicians trained in the use of radiation—use X rays and gamma rays to examine internal body structures in order to diagnose disease (see RADIATION; RADIOLOGY).

The science of radiography began with the discovery of X rays by Wilhelm Roentgen in 1895 (see ROENTGEN, WILHELM CONRAD; X RAY). The rays are used to produce images on photographic film, a fluorescent screen, or a video monitor (similar to a television screen). The pictures produced are called radiographs. They are really shadow pictures. The densest parts of the object absorb the most rays and thus cast shadows. Because a radiograph is normally a transparent negative, the densest parts show up as light areas when viewed against a light box.

The use of X rays is important in medicine. X rays pass easily through the soft, fleshy parts of the body, but the denser bones absorb the rays. Thus, broken bones and dislocated joints show up well on a radiograph. Foreign objects such as bullets or swallowed coins are readily seen as well. Dental radiographs reveal cavities in teeth. Chest radiographs may reveal enlargement of the heart or show tumors (abnormal growths) or other diseases of the lungs.

Because many of the body's soft tissues and organs do not show up well with X rays, a contrast agent or medium is often used. This is a substance that is radio-opaque—that is, opaque to X rays—and is introduced into the body to outline an organ or a cavity. For example, a "barium meal," a thick suspension of barium sulfate powder, may be used to show the esophagus, stomach, and intestines. Other radio-opaque liquids may be injected to show the flow of blood in the arteries and veins or to show the inside of the kidneys or gallbladder.

In computed tomography, also called CAT or CT scanning, X rays and computers are used to create precise images of separate overlapping organs (see COMPUTED TOMOGRAPHY). Gamma rays are used in nuclear medicine procedures (see GAMMA RAY; NUCLEAR MEDICINE). The rays are emitted by radioactive substances taken into the body and are scanned by special devices, such as scintillation cameras (see RADIOACTIVITY). These scans are used to study organ function.

Radiography is also widely used in industry. It can be used to examine the inside of welded joints to check for defects. It can be used to search for cracks in metal components, such as aircraft parts or sections of oil pipeline. X rays are also used at airports to search baggage for hidden weapons.

RADIOGRAPHY

Radiography has a variety of uses. Shown at top is a mummified ibis (a kind of bird) from ancient Egypt. At right is a radiograph of the ibis, which will be studied by archeologists.

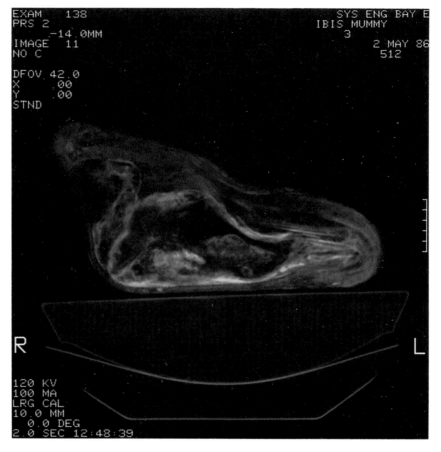

The X-ray machines used in medical radiography do not normally produce X rays that are penetrating enough to examine the inside of metal objects. For this purpose, intense rays of short wavelength are needed. Instead of using an X-ray machine, an industrial radiographer may use a source of gamma rays. A small quantity of radioactive material in a special lead container is used to direct a beam of gamma rays through the object to a photographic plate.

Exposure to large amounts of high-energy radiation is dangerous. People who work with X rays and gamma rays take special precautions to avoid such exposure.

RADIOLARIAN (rā´dē ō lâr´ē ən) A radiolarian is a tiny marine (sea-living) protozoan, similar to an ameba, except for having a delicate, glasslike skeleton made of silica (see AMEBA; PROTOZOA; SILICA). The skeleton usually forms an intricate network with numerous spines projecting from it. Radiolarians measure about 0.20 in. [0.5 cm] in diameter.

The one-celled organism consists of a central capsule containing the nucleus, surrounded by a layer of frothy cytoplasm (see CELL). Tiny strands extend from this outer layer to trap other organisms for food.

The frothy cytoplasm also contains other tiny organisms living in symbiosis with the radiolarian (see SYMBIOSIS). When radiolarians die, their skeletons sink to the ocean floor. Large areas of the deep sea are covered with a layer of this radiolarian ooze. *See also* OOZE.

RADIOLOGY (rā′dē ŏl′ə jē) Radiology is the branch of medicine that uses radiation and other forms of energy to diagnose and treat disease. Radiologists are physicians specially trained in radiology (see RADIATION).

In diagnostic radiology, special procedures are done and special equipment is used to examine the patient's organs, bones, and other internal structures. The diagnostic radiologist reviews the images that are created by the examinations. The radiologist can then determine what, if anything, is wrong with the patient.

The patient may undergo an X-ray examination.

An X-ray examination of the lungs (a chest X-ray examination) is one of the most common radiologic studies (see X RAY). The patient may undergo a computed tomography (CAT or CT) examination. CT combines the use of X rays and computers to produce imaged "slices" of anatomy (see COMPUTED TOMOGRAPHY). Gamma rays are also used to diagnose disease, as part of nuclear medicine procedures (see GAMMA RAY; NUCLEAR MEDICINE; RADIOGRAPHY).

Patients also may undergo diagnostic procedures that do not require the use of X rays or gamma rays. Ultrasound imaging uses sound that cannot be heard to produce pictures of internal organs (see ULTRASOUND). Magnetic resonance imaging (MRI) uses a magnetic field and radio signals to create images (see MAGNETIC RESONANCE IMAGING).

In radiation therapy, radiation-generating equipment and radioactive materials are used to treat cancer patients (see RADIATION THERAPY). The radiation therapist, also called a radiation oncologist, oversees the radiation treatment of cancer patients.

Technologists and physicists work with diagnostic radiologists as well as with radiation therapists. Technologists often prepare the patients for the diagnostic examination or cancer treatment. They also may operate the equipment used in diagnosing

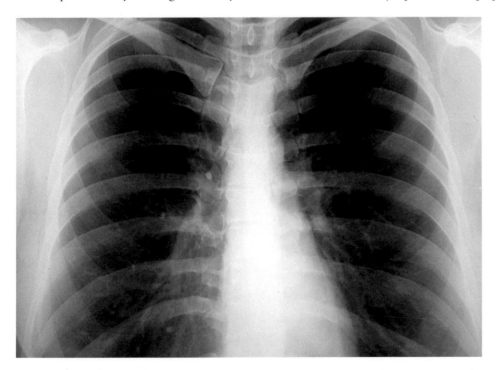

RADIOLOGY

This X ray of a woman's chest shows the spine, rib cage, and part of the collarbone.

or treating the patient. Radiologic physicists are scientists who specialize in the use of radiation in the diagnosis and treatment of disease. Radiologic physicists have either a master's or doctoral degree. Radiologic physicists perform tests on radiation equipment to make sure that the radiation is focused properly and in appropriate amounts during diagnostic examinations and during treatment. In radiation therapy, physicists help plan treatments based on their knowledge of the properties of radiation and its effects on human tissues.

RADIOSONDE (rā′dē ō sŏnd′) A radiosonde is a device that takes measurements in the upper atmosphere. A radiosonde consists of meteorological (weather science) instruments carried into the atmosphere by a helium or hydrogen balloon (see BALLOON). The instruments aboard the radiosonde record the temperature, dew point, humidity, barometric (atmospheric) pressure, and wind speed and direction at various heights above the earth. The data obtained is sent by radio back to weather stations on the earth. The measurements taken by a radiosonde are called soundings.

Meteorologists can determine the state of jet streams by using radiosondes. The information is used to predict the formation and movements of storms and other weather systems (see JET STREAM). Radiosondes also send information that can be used to determine the stability of the atmosphere. If the atmosphere is very stable, a meteorologist may predict high air pollution levels. If the atmosphere is very unstable, a meteorologist may predict thunderstorms and, possibly, tornadoes.

See also ATMOSPHERE; METEOROLOGY; WEATHER.

RADISH (răd′ĭsh) The radish is an annual plant of the mustard family, Brassicaceae or Cruciferae (see ANNUAL PLANT; MUSTARD FAMILY). It is grown widely for its edible root, which is used as an appetizer and in salads.

Radish roots vary in shape, size, and color, depending on the variety. The variety most commonly grown in the United States is round with a

RADISH
There are many different kinds of radishes, which are all members of the mustard family. This variety is generally used raw in salads.

bright red skin. The flesh is white and firm, somewhat like that of a potato. However, it has a distinctive sharp taste.

Radishes grow throughout the year in mild, cool climates. Most radishes grown in the United States are harvested in the spring. In Japan and China, people grow a winter radish, called a daikon.

RADIUM (rā′dē əm) Radium (Ra) is a radioactive white metallic element (see ELEMENT; RADIOACTIVITY). Radium was discovered in 1898 by the French physicists Marie and Pierre Curie (see CURIE FAMILY). It occurs in very small amounts in uranium ores such as pitchblende (see PITCHBLENDE; URANIUM). Radium once was used in medicine to destroy cancer growths and had industrial uses as well. However, radium has largely been replaced by less expensive and safer sources of radiation for such uses. Radium must be handled very carefully, as it can destroy the body's cells. Skin damaged in this way is sometimes called "burned."

There are twenty-six isotopes of radium (see ISOTOPE). The most common is radium-226.

Its half-life is 1,620 years (see HALF-LIFE).

Radium's atomic number is 88, and its relative atomic mass is 226.026. It melts at 1,290°F [700°C] and boils at 2,080°F [1,140°C]. Its relative density is about 5.

See also RADON; RELATIVE DENSITY.

RADIUS (rā′dē əs)

In human beings, the radius is the bone of the forearm on the thumb side. It is shorter than the other bone of the forearm, called the ulna (see ULNA). The radius moves around and crosses the ulna as the hand is turned to cause the palm to face backward. All land vertebrates have a bone equivalent to the radius (see VERTEBRATE).

In the geometry of a circle or a sphere, the radius is the distance from the center to any point on the circumference or surface.

See also GEOMETRY.

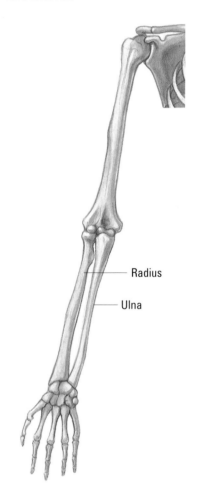

RADIUS

The radius is one of the bones of the forearm (the other bone is called the ulna). The radius is on the same side of the arm as the thumb.

RADON (rā′dŏn)

Radon (Rn) is a radioactive gas. It is the heaviest of the noble gases (see ELEMENT; NOBLE GAS; RADIOACTIVITY).

Radon was discovered in 1900 by the German scientist Friedrich Dorn. He found that the gas is given off when the metallic element radium decays (see RADIUM). Because it soon decays into other elements, radon occurs only in very small amounts. There are twenty-eight isotopes of radon. The longest-lived is radon-222. Its half-life is just under four days (see HALF-LIFE; ISOTOPE). Radon is used in medical treatments for cancer (see RADIATION THERAPY).

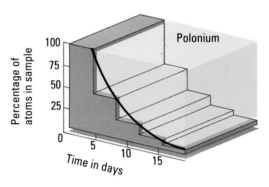

RADON

A radioactive substance decays in a regular way. The graph shows how the amount of a sample of the radioactive gas radon decreases as it decays into polonium.

When radium in the soil decays to radon, the noble gas seeps up to the surface. The radioactive gas may get into the air of homes and other buildings through cracks in their foundations, or through dirt floors or drains in basements. The National Council on Radiation Protection and Measurements estimates that radon delivers a dose of 200 millirem to a person in a typical home during a year (see REM). This is about twice that received from other environmental sources of radiation.

Certain homes are built on soil that contains large amounts of radium or radium products. The air in these homes may contain larger amounts of radon than normal. The Environmental Protection Agency recommends that all homes be tested to determine whether excessive levels of radon are present. Radon's atomic number is 86. It liquefies at -79.2°F [-61.8°C] and becomes solid at -96°F [-71 °C].

A railroad is a two-railed track that carries trains of cars along a permanent route. However, the term *railroad* generally includes not only the track but the land on which it is located, the rolling stock (locomotives, passenger cars, and freight cars), and the buildings of the company that operates it.

The railroad is one of the most important means of transportation. Every day, thousands of trains travel along railroad tracks throughout the world. Some trains carry passengers. Others haul grain, lumber, coal, machinery, and many other products. The fastest trains reach speeds of over 230 m.p.h. [370 kph]. An average freight train can haul thousands of tons of goods across a continent.

There are railroads in almost every country. The world's longest rail line is in Russia. It extends about 5,600 mi. [9,010 km] and connects Moscow with Vladivostok. Private companies own and operate the major railroads in the United States. However, in most other countries, the central government operates the railroads. One of Canada's two major railroads is government owned. A private company operates the other one.

How railroads serve the public Railroads provide two main types of service: passenger service and freight service. Passenger service is divided into two categories: commuter trains and intercity trains. About 75 percent of all U.S. rail passengers ride commuter trains. These trains carry hundreds of thousands of suburban residents to and from work in large cities each working day. Two large U.S. commuter operations are in New York City and Chicago. Commuter trains also serve San Francisco, Paris, London, Tokyo, Moscow, Toronto, and many other cities throughout the world. The average commuter train carries as many passengers when full as a thousand automobiles. Thus, commuter trains help relieve rush-hour auto traffic jams on city expressways.

Some countries have unusually fast and efficient intercity passenger trains. The fastest passenger trains in the world operate in France. High speed trains travel up to 167 m.p.h. [269 kph] between Paris and Lyon, and up to 205 m.p.h. [330 kph] between Paris and some of the cities in western France. Japan's passenger trains are also among the

FIRST RAILROAD
The first passenger railroad ran between Stockton and Darlington in the north of England. It opened in 1825 with a train hauled by George Stephenson's steam locomotive called *Locomotion.*

fastest in the world. Many Japanese trains, for example, travel at an average speed of more than 100 m.p.h. [160 kph]. The fastest Japanese trains run between Tokyo and Osaka. They make the 320-mi. [515-km] trip in three hours—about half the time required to make the trip by automobile. The same rail trip in the United States would require at least double that amount of time. High-speed passenger trains also service most cities in Britain and the rest of Europe. Canada has a well-known fast passenger train called the "Rapido." It runs between Toronto and Montreal, a distance of 335 mi. [539 km], at an average speed of 80 m.p.h. [130 kph]. Metroliners, the electric passenger trains that run between New York City and Washington, D.C., are the fastest U.S. passenger trains. They average about 80 m.p.h. [130 kph] over the 225-mi. [362-km] run. The U.S. government formed a corporation called Amtrak in 1970. Amtrak operates almost all the intercity passenger trains in the United States.

About 95 percent of all money earned by U.S. railroads comes from hauling freight. The largest freight trains have two hundred or more cars. The average freight train has about seventy cars, and carries approximately 1,800 tons [1,630 metric

AMERICAN LOCOMOTIVE

A typical American locomotive of the mid-1800s had four driving wheels behind a four-wheeled bogie (below). The bogie wheels swiveled to help the train go around curves more easily. The locomotive burned wood as fuel and had a cowcatcher at the front to push obstacles off the track.

DIESEL LOCOMOTIVE

Diesel locomotives began to replace steam locomotives in the 1940s. This train (left) carried passengers 2,900 mi. [4,675 km] between Montreal and Vancouver.

SUBWAY TRAIN

Subway trains, powered by electric motors, are common in many large cities. The train below is made of aluminum, with stainless steel seats to reduce the risk of fire. It runs on Hong Kong's Mass Transit Railway.

TRACK MAINTENANCE
Railroad track maintenance is important for safety. In the photograph above, new crossties are being placed under the rails they support.

tons] of goods. American railroads are carrying more freight than ever before. However, most of them haul a smaller share of the total intercity freight traffic than in the past. Trailer trucks and airplanes have cut into their workload.

Today, U.S. railroads carry around 50 percent of the intercity freight. They have tried two methods to regain their leadership: "piggyback" service and "containerization." Piggyback service is the use of flatcars to haul trucks loaded with freight. This way, a trucking line can have many trucks transported to another city for a fraction of the cost required to haul them individually over the highways. Containers are large, rectangular metal boxes filled with freight. They are transferred from flatcars to specially designed ships and trucks.

Tracks The rails and crossties that make up railway track are laid along a roadbed. The roadbed is land that has been prepared as a foundation for the

track. The roadbed follows the route planned for the railroad. The surface layer of the roadbed is ballast, or crushed rock. The rails, which are made of steel in an I-beam shape, are secured to wood, concrete, or steel crossties that rest on the ballast. The rails are in 39-ft. [12-m] sections and traditionally have been joined end to end by joint bars, also called fish plates. The small gaps between the joints make the familiar clickety-clack sounds as the train wheels pass over them. Most U.S. railroads are now replacing these rails with rails that have welded joints. The new rails eliminate the noise and give a smoother ride.

The distance the rails are set apart from one another (the width) is known as the gauge. Standard gauge, or width, in the United States and Canada is 4 ft. 8^1/$_2$ in. [1.44 m].

Rolling stock Most trains are pulled by a locomotive, but some are pushed. Locomotives that haul passenger and freight cars are called road locomotives. Locomotives that move cars from track to track in rail yards are called switching locomotives (see LOCOMOTIVE).

Passenger and freight cars have something in common. Each car has a device called a coupler at each end. The coupler links one car to another. Both types of cars also have air brakes, which are connected to a master control in the locomotive (see BRAKE). On most passenger trains, the cars consist mainly of coaches. Coaches generally seat from 50 to 90 passengers. Some commuter trains have double-deck (two-level) coaches that seat 150 to 170 persons. Other types of cars that may be found in passenger trains are cars that offer refreshments (often called club cars) and dining cars. Intercity passenger trains also may have sleeping cars, baggage cars, and dome cars. A dome car has

FREIGHT TRAIN

Carrying freight has always been an important source of income for railroads. Here two powerful diesel locomotives haul a long, heavy freight train in California.

RAILROAD PRESERVATION
Steam locomotives have been phased out throughout most of North America and Europe. But in some countries, railroad enthusiasts have bought old railroads and rebuilt locomotives to get them back into working order. This preserved locomotive is running on a railroad track in southern England.

a dome-shaped upper level enclosed in glass for sightseeing. Dome cars are generally found on long-distance passenger trains in the western part of the United States.

Freight cars range from enclosed boxcars for carrying general freight to specially designed flatcars for new automobiles. Tank cars are used to carry various liquids. Open-top cars carry bulk materials, such as coal.

Traffic control Railroads use lighted signals and various other devices to control train traffic. Most traffic signals consist of colored lights mounted on poles alongside or over the tracks. Just as in automobile traffic signals, red means stop, green means proceed, and yellow means proceed with caution. Sometimes, the signal is in the form of a semaphore. A semaphore consists of a set of movable arms mounted on a pole. Each position of the arms is a different signal to the engineer driving the train.

Most railroads use a block signal system. This system is designed to make sure that trains keep a safe distance from one another. It divides the railroad route into blocks that range from 1 to 2 mi. [1.6 to 3.2 km] long. Only one train is allowed to be in a block at a time. Colored light signals control the entering of trains into each block. When a train is in a block, signal lights warn other trains not to enter. The signals usually operate automatically.

In the United States, the federal government requires automatic block systems on all tracks where passenger trains travel at 60 m.p.h. [97 kph] and over. Automatic signals are also required where freight trains travel at 50 m.p.h. [80 kph]

or over. One of the most advanced automatic signal systems is called Centralized Traffic Control (CTC). In this system, trains trip automatic block signals when they enter and leave blocks, but all the signals can be controlled from a central control station. If an operator in the central control station sees two trains heading for a collision, he or she can flip a switch that moves a track switch, causing one of the trains to pull off the main track onto a siding to allow the other train to pass. A siding is a short length of track just off a main line. The switching operation is accomplished with a short piece of curved track that swings into place automatically and makes the train change direction. Some switches can be operated by hand.

In addition to lighted signals, some trains also have a safety device called automatic train stop (ATS). It automatically puts on the train's brakes if the engineer fails to notice a stop or caution signal. Also, many locomotives contain two-way radios so that crew members can communicate with distant stations and central control points.

History The first public railroads began in England in the 1820s and 1830s. They used steam engines to haul wagons loaded with freight or passengers. Other countries also had steam-powered railroads by the mid-1800s. The first steam railroad line in the United States was a 6-mi. [10-km] length of track between Charleston and Hamburg, South Carolina. A steam locomotive called *The Best Friend of Charleston* began making regular runs in 1831.

The number of railroads in the United States multiplied rapidly after 1830. Railroad lines began to crisscross the country, opening up vast new territories for settlement and economic growth. Railroads were particularly important in developing the western part of the country. American railroads made enormous profits from the 1870s into the 1920s. The country's financial leaders battled for control of the richest railroad companies.

However, the Great Depression of the 1930s brought financial ruin to many railroads. Many

RAILROAD HISTORY

The railroads linked various regions of the United States in the 1800s. It became possible to cross the country in far less time than ever before.

were forced out of business. The 1940s and World War II (1939–1945) saw a recovery period for the nation's railroads. They aided the war effort by hauling more goods than ever before.

Since that boom period of the 1940s, the railroads have been in decline again. Heavy competition from airlines, trucks, buses, and automobiles has cut into their passenger and freight business. In 1976, six bankrupt railroads located in the northeastern part of the country were reorganized into a private corporation by the federal government. The corporation is called Consolidated Rail Corporation (ConRail). The outlook for U.S. railroads is still uncertain.

See also MAGNETIC LEVITATION VEHICLE.

RAIN Rain is liquid water that falls from the clouds to the ground. Rain is a form of precipitation (see PRECIPITATION). Rain is the earth's major source of fresh water. Without rain, life on Earth would be impossible.

How rain forms The sun's heat is constantly causing evaporation of water from the oceans and other bodies of water and from the moist earth. This evaporated water, called water vapor, is always present in varying amounts in the air (see EVAPORATION). As the air rises, it cools and cannot hold as much water vapor. At a temperature known as the dew point, the water vapor condenses on tiny particles in the air, forming water droplets. These particles, called condensation nuclei, include soot, dust, and salt (see CONDENSATION; DEW POINT). The water droplets gather together, forming clouds. If the water droplets become supercooled—that is, they remain liquid below the freezing point of 32°F [0°C]—they combine, and may be heavy enough to fall to the ground as rain or snow (see SUPERCOOLING). If the temperature drops low enough, the water droplets may form ice crystals, which may fall to the ground as hail or snow.

An important condition of rain formation is the lifting of air. This lifting results in cooling and a decrease in pressure and thus the condensation of water vapor. Lifting happens in several ways.

Orographic lifting occurs when air is forced upward by a natural barrier, such as a mountain. As the air rises, it cools. Often, one side of a mountain receives much heavier rain or snow than the other side. This happens because the clouds release all their moisture before getting over the mountain. This condition occurs in the Rocky Mountains and the Himalayas.

Frontal lifting occurs in the temperate regions of the world. A front is the boundary between two different air masses (see FRONT). The heavy, cool air of one air mass pushes beneath the warmer air of the other air mass, causing the warm air to rise. The water vapor in the warm air condenses and eventually falls as rain or snow. This type of lifting causes the precipitation associated with frontal cyclones (see CYCLONE).

Convectional lifting occurs in the tropics and during the summer in temperate regions. The sun heats the air near the earth's surface, causing moisture to evaporate and the lighter, heated air to rise, cool, and lose its remaining moisture as rain. The precipitation occurs in the late afternoon or evening, during thunderstorms (see CONVECTION; THUNDERSTORM).

RAIN

An important condition of rain formation is the orographic lifting of air by a natural barrier such as a mountain (top). Frontal lifting occurs when the heavy, cool air of one air mass pushes under the warmer air of another air mass, causing it to rise (center). Convectional lifting occurs when the sun heats the air near the ground, causing moisture to evaporate and the less dense, warm air to rise (bottom).

Distribution of rainfall Rainfall is greatest in the tropics, where there is a yearly average of about

100 in. [250 cm]. The temperate regions average about 34 in. [83 cm] a year. The polar regions receive very little precipitation. Deserts also receive very little rain. For example, Death Valley, in California, has an average annual rainfall of 1.78 in. [4.52 cm]. Some regions have adequate precipitation but sometimes have extended periods of unusually dry weather. Such a dry period is called a drought.

See also CLIMATE; DROUGHT; RAINMAKING; WEATHER.

RAINBOW A rainbow is an arch of colored light that appears when the sun shines through a rain shower. As the sun's rays pass through raindrops and are reflected from them, the light is bent and separated into different colors (see LIGHT; REFRACTION OF LIGHT). Thus, each raindrop acts as a tiny prism (see PRISM). A person sees a particular color reflected from each raindrop depending on the angle between the person, the raindrop, and the sun. All the raindrops at a certain angle will appear red, all at another angle will appear orange, and so on.

A complete rainbow has a primary bow and a secondary bow. The primary bow is more brilliant. Its colors are violet on the inside, then indigo (violet blue), blue, green, yellow, orange, and red on the outside. The colors of the dimmer secondary bow are reversed. Red is on the inside, and violet is on the outside. The secondary bow is located above the primary bow.

Rainbows form in the part of the sky opposite the sun. Rainbows may also form when sunlight strikes the spray from a waterfall or even water from a garden hose.

See also SPECTRUM. PROJECT 44, 52

Primary rainbow
Light ray
Total internal reflection
Water vapor
Refraction
Raindrop
Refraction

Secondary rainbow
Second internal reflection
First internal reflection

RAINBOW

A rainbow (left) is formed when a ray of light from the sun is reflected and refracted (bent) as it enters a raindrop. The different wavelengths (colors) of light are refracted differently and spread out to form a primary rainbow (above top). In a secondary rainbow, the light is reflected twice in the raindrop, so the colors are reversed (above bottom).

RAIN FOREST

A rain forest is a forest of mostly evergreens in a climate that is constantly wet. An evergreen is a tree or shrub that has leaves throughout the year. Most of the world's rain forests are made up of broad-leaved evergreen trees and are found in tropical, subtropical, and temperate regions. However, some wet conifer forests, such as those found in Alaska, California, Washington, and New Zealand, are also called rain forests (see CLIMATE; CONIFER; EVERGREEN; TREE).

The largest rain forests are tropical and are located near the equator, such as in western and central Africa, Indonesia, Malaysia, and New Guinea. The largest tropical rain forest, the Amazon rain forest, covers about one-third of South America. Temperatures in tropical rain forests range from about 68° to 93°F [20° to 34°C]. Thunderstorms are very common and occur almost every day in some areas. The annual rainfall in a tropical rain forest is at least 80 in. [200 cm].

Tropical rain forests have a wider variety of animal and plant species than is found in any other kind of forest in the world. For example, thousands of species of birds and insects dwell in tropical rain forests. The animals and plants have very delicate and complex relationships with one another. The most common plants in tropical rain forests are vines; hardwood trees, such as mahoganies; and small flowering plants, such as orchids and bromeliads that grow as epiphytes on the trees (see EPIPHYTE; ORCHID FAMILY). The tallest trees form a covering of leaves called the upper canopy. The upper canopy may be 100 to 150 ft. [30 to 46 m] above the ground. Smaller trees form lower canopies. The shade from the trees prevents about 99 percent of the sunlight from reaching the ground. Thus, few low-growing plants are found in the forest. However, the ground near rivers and in clearings may have many such plants. These areas are sometimes called jungles. Much of the animal life in the rain forest lives in the canopies. To study the organisms in the canopies, scientists have to use unusual means, such as hot-air balloons or construction cranes.

The diverse plant life in tropical rain forests provides many valuable products for people, such as hardwoods, herbs, fibers, rattan, rubber, and chemicals for drugs (see DRUG; FIBER; HERB; RUBBER). The demand for these products is increasing around the world. The rain forests are rapidly being cleared to try to meet this demand. The rain forests are also being cleared for farming. This is in spite of the fact that rain forests usually have only a thin layer of soil that is poor for farming.

Scientists estimate that over 31,000 acres [12,550 hectares] of tropical rain forests are

destroyed every day due to clearing. The clearing of rain forests has and will have effects felt around the world. For example, many species of animals may die out because of the loss of habitat (see EXTINCTION). The loss of animals affects the food chain (see FOOD CHAIN). The decrease in plant life means less photosynthesis. Less photosynthesis means less oxygen is produced and less carbon dioxide is taken out of the air (see PHOTOSYNTHESIS). Carbon dioxide is one of the main gases behind the greenhouse effect, which many scientists believe is leading to global warming (see GREENHOUSE EFFECT).

If the present rate of clearing continues, scientists predict that the world's tropical rain forests will disappear within one hundred years. Scientists also predict that the greenhouse effect will cause drastic changes in temperature and rainfall patterns. This means that tropical rain forests that have been cleared may not be able to grow back. The cleared land may become desert.

North American rain forests are also threatened. In the late 1980s, world demand for North American lumber grew. Much of the population near these rain forests depends on the lumber industry for jobs. Because of these two facts, North American forests continue to be cleared (see LUMBER).

There are efforts around the world, however, to save the rain forests. Some countries, such as China, India, Thailand, and Nepal, already have reforestation programs in place. In these programs, young trees or seeds are planted. The United Nations and the World Bank have proposed a plan to spend billions of dollars in the 1990s to plant trees around the world.

See also DEFORESTATION.

RAIN FORESTS UNDER THREAT

Rain forests are one of the earth's most complex and important environments. They provide a home for countless species of plants and animals. The forest illustrated at left is in central Granada, West Indies. Today, many of the rain forests are being destroyed by timber cutters or by farmers clearing land to raise cattle. The photograph above shows the disastrous results in a former rain forest in Brazil.

RAIN GAUGE A rain gauge is an instrument used to measure the amount of rainfall. There are several types of rain gauges. A common type is an open cylinder into which rain falls. The side of the cylinder is marked in inches or millimeters. Some rain gauges are made to prevent the evaporation of the rain water. Others require the rainwater to be emptied from the instrument and measured elsewhere. Rain gauges are usually placed in open areas where there is no interference from trees or buildings.

See also METEOROLOGY.　　　　PROJECT 25

RAINMAKING Rainmaking, or cloud seeding, is the process by which chemicals are put into certain clouds to cause rainfall. There are several different rainmaking methods.

At temperatures below 32°F [0°C], clouds can be seeded with frozen carbon dioxide (dry ice). This way works with clouds made up of supercooled water droplets. Supercooled water remains liquid below the freezing point, 32°F [0°C] (see CLOUD; PRECIPITATION; RAIN; SUPERCOOLING). Dry ice causes the temperature to drop even farther. This makes the supercooled water droplets form large ice crystals, which fall to the ground as rain or snow.

Silver iodide crystals are also used to produce rain from a cloud of supercooled water droplets. The water forms ice crystals around the silver iodide. When the crystals are large enough, they fall to the ground as rain or snow.

A liquid fertilizer consisting of ammonium nitrate and urea is used to make rain from clouds with temperatures above the freezing point. The fertilizer is sprayed from an airplane beneath the cloud. Water droplets form around the ammonium nitrate and urea particles and then fall to the earth as rain.

There is much controversy about rainmaking. Many people feel that an increase in rainfall in one place reduces the rainfall in another. Other people, however, feel that rainmaking is an invaluable aid to farmers.

RAISIN A raisin is a grape that has been dried by the sun or by some artificial method. Most raisins are made from thin-skinned, seedless yellow grapes that have a high sugar content. Raisins have been a popular food for thousands of years. Until the late 1800s, most raisins were produced in the Mediterranean countries. By the mid-1890s, however, California had become the world's leading producer of raisins. In the United States, only California produces raisins commercially. Its yearly output is about 350 million lb. [160 million kg].

Raisins have a high nutritional value. They are rich in carbohydrates, iron, several other minerals, and vitamins A, B_1, and B_2. Raisins may be eaten raw. They may also be cooked and used in other foods.

See also GRAPE.

RAISIN

Raisins are made by drying grapes. They are rich in carbohydrates, minerals, and vitamins.

RAMSAY, SIR WILLIAM (1852–1916) Sir William Ramsay was a British chemist who discovered a group of gases called the noble gases (see NOBLE GAS). Ramsay worked on the noble gases with another British scientist, John Rayleigh. In 1894, they removed the gases oxygen, nitrogen, and carbon dioxide from air. They were left with a small amount of an unreactive gas. They showed that it was a new element. They called it argon (see ELEMENT). In 1898, Ramsay liquefied air and then separated out the gases by fractional distillation (see DISTILLATION). Working with M.W. Travers, he discovered that air also contains the gases neon, krypton, and xenon. In 1895, he discovered helium, another noble gas. For his work on the noble gases, Ramsay won the 1904 Nobel Prize for chemistry.

RANGE FINDER A range finder is a device used to measure distances. Optical range finders are used by surveyors and military people. Some cameras also have optical range finders (see CAMERA). Radar is also a range-finding system. It measures the time lapse of an electromagnetic echo and translates the time into distance (see RADAR).

Military range finders are usually long tubes with eyepieces at the center. Lenses and prisms are located at each end of the tube (see LENS; PRISM). The operator looks through the eyepieces and adjusts the prisms so that the target can be sighted through both ends of the tube at the same time.

The difference in direction of the two lines of sight is called the parallactic angle. The angle depends on the distance to the target. The angle is measured on a dial from which the distance of the target can be read directly.

Two types of range finders are the coincidence type and the stereoscopic type. In the coincidence type, the operator looks through a single eyepiece and sees two images of the target. By the operator's turning a knob, the two images move together. When this happens, the distance to the target can be read on a dial.

The operator of a stereoscopic range finder looks through a pair of eyepieces. The operator sees a single image of the target and also a marker that

RANGE FINDER

Many modern range-finding systems make use of radar. A series of high-frequency radio pulses are sent out and any reflections detected when they bounce back (below right). The time the pulses take to return gives a measure of the range. Radar information is displayed on a television-type screen (below left).

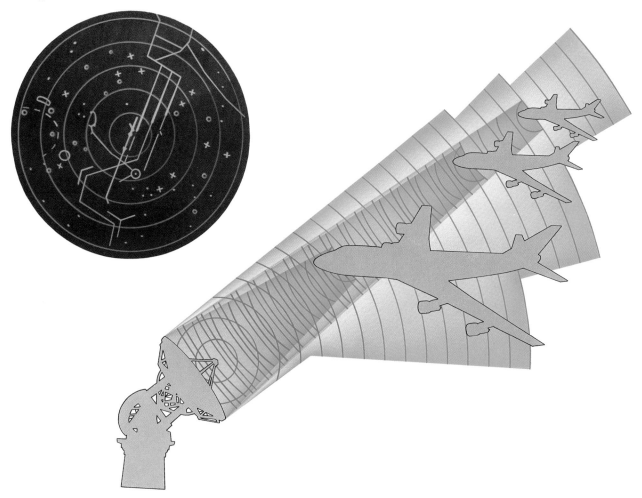

seems to be floating in space near the target. The operator turns a knob until the marker seems to be the same distance away as the target. Then the distance is read on a dial.

During World War II (1939–1945), radar largely replaced optical range finders, because it can measure ranges more accurately. More recently, the military has used laser range finders, which measure the time needed for a pulse of light to travel to and from a target. Laser range finders work both during the day and at night and can measure long distances.

See also LASER.

RARE EARTH ELEMENT Rare earth elements are a group of fifteen metallic elements with very similar properties (see ELEMENT). Their atomic numbers range from 57 to 71. The rare earth elements also are known as the lanthanides, after the first element of the series, which is named lanthanum. Many rare earth elements are found in minerals called the rare earth minerals. The most important of these are monazite and gadolinite.

The rare earth elements are similar to each other because their atoms have a similar structure. An atom has a central core called a nucleus. It is surrounded by tiny orbiting particles called electrons (see ATOM). These electrons are arranged in shells. In the rare earth elements, the arrangement of electrons is the same in all the shells except one. That shell can hold up to fourteen electrons. Lanthanum has no electrons in that shell. The next element has one electron in the shell. The next has two, and so on. The last rare earth element, lutetium, has a full shell of fourteen electrons.

RASPBERRY (răz′bĕr′ē) The raspberry is a prickly shrub growing in the form of upright canes. It belongs to genus *Rubus* in the rose family. There are several species (see ROSE FAMILY). The shrubs grow throughout the Northern Hemisphere. In the United States, they grow in the northern coastal states and near the Great Lakes. The raspberry fruit is a cluster of tiny, juicy red or yellow drupelets, each of which surrounds a little pip containing a seed (see DRUPE). The fruit grows around the

receptacle, from which it is easily separated (see RECEPTACLE). This characteristic is what makes the raspberry different from its close relative, the blackberry. The blackberry fruit does not separate easily from the receptacle. The raspberry shrub produces fruit beginning in its second year. The canes die after producing fruit, but new ones grow to take their place. The fruit is rich in iron and vitamin C. It is eaten fresh, preserved as jam or jelly, or cooked into foods. There are many cultivated varieties.

RASPBERRY
The raspberry is a popular fruit, grown in temperate climates. The "berry" is actually a cluster of many drupelets, each containing a single seed.

RAT The rat is a furry mammal that looks like a mouse and, like the mouse, is a rodent (see RODENT). However, the rat is larger than the mouse. In fact, the smallest rats are longer and weigh more than the largest mice.

There are more than one hundred kinds of rats. The black rat and the brown rat are the best-known species. The black rat originally came from southeast Asia and the brown rat from China, but they have now followed humans to all parts of the world. They carry fleas that transmit dangerous diseases (see FLEA). Most other kinds of rats live in areas not inhabited by people. All species of rats have a slender, scaly or hairy tail and long, sharp claws.

Black rats grow from 6 to 9 in. [15 to 23 cm] in length, not including the tail. The tail is longer than the body. A black rat's fur, which is soft, may be black, grayish brown, or gray. The underside

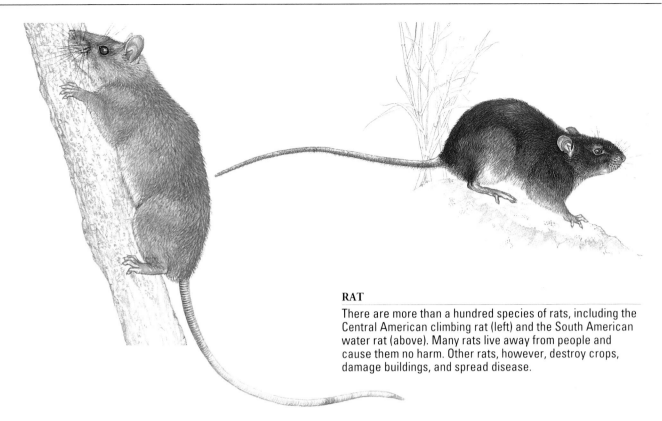

RAT
There are more than a hundred species of rats, including the Central American climbing rat (left) and the South American water rat (above). Many rats live away from people and cause them no harm. Other rats, however, destroy crops, damage buildings, and spread disease.

may be gray, white, yellow, or a combination of these colors. "Roof rats" and "ship rats" are other names for black rats.

Brown rats range from about 8 to 11 in. [20 to 29 cm] in length, not including the tail, which is shorter than the body. These rats vary in color from brownish gray to reddish gray. Brown rats have coarse fur. "Barn rat," "sewer rat," and "house rat" are common names for brown rats.

Both brown and black rats live in groups. Certain rats have control over others. Members of both species build nests in or near buildings. Both species eat almost any kind of plant or small animal, feeding mostly at night.

Most black and brown rats mate all year. The females give birth to three to six litters each year. Each litter may range from six to nine babies. Because they have so many enemies, few rats live more than a year in their natural surroundings. Animals that prey on rats include cats, dogs, owls, and snakes.

In the United States, rats cause damage totaling hundreds of millions of dollars each year. Black and brown rats destroy eggs, fruit, grain, and vegetables. They also attack farm animals. They sometimes gnaw on furniture and lead pipes and can cause fires by chewing on electric wires. Rats have been known to attack human beings.

RATIO (rā′shō) A ratio is a mathematical expression that gives the relationship of two different quantities. For example, suppose two salespeople have each sold a certain number of products. One has sold seven products, and the other has sold five products. The relationship between the numbers of products can be written as a ratio—7:5. This expression is read *seven to five.* The first number of the ratio is called the antecedent, and the second number is called the consequent. In this example, 7 is the antecedent and 5 is the consequent.

Fractions and percentages are also considered ratios. For example 20/100 or 20% can also be written 20:100. Ratios help scientists express relationships about what they are studying. For example, a ratio would show the difference in amounts of two substances in a solution.

See also ARITHMETIC; FRACTION; MATHEMATICS; NUMBER; PERCENT.

RATTLESNAKE A rattlesnake is a very poisonous snake. It gets its name from the large, hollow, conelike scales at the tip of its tail. When the tail

RATTLESNAKE

The rattlesnake gets its name from the cluster of scales at the tip of its tail. When the snake moves its tail back and forth, the scales make a noise that usually scares away enemies.

moves back and forth, the scales, or rattles, make a loud buzzing noise. The noise usually scares away enemies and also warns larger animals to keep away. The rattlesnake adds a new scale to its rattle every time it sheds its skin, but the older scales gradually wear away, and even old snakes rarely have more than about twelve scales in their rattles. There are about thirty species of rattlesnakes. Rattlesnakes are found in all of the United States except Hawaii, Alaska, Delaware, and Maine. They are also found in southern Canada and in Mexico, Central America, and South America. The largest rattlesnake is the diamondback rattlesnake, which can grow to lengths of 72 in. [183 cm]. The smallest rattlesnake is the western pygmy rattlesnake, which grows to a length of 20 in. [51 cm]. Rattlesnakes live in all types of areas—deserts, mountains, prairies, forests, and swamps. Young rattlesnakes eat frogs and lizards, but mature rattlesnakes feed mainly on rodents and other warm-blooded animals. The snakes belong to a group known as pit vipers (see VIPER). A heat-sensitive pit on each side of the head enables them to detect the warmth of their prey and guides them to it.

RAVEN A raven is a large bird—the largest of all the songbirds or perching birds. It belongs to the crow family, Corvidae. From a distance, a raven looks like a crow. It is all black but usually larger than a crow. In flight its tail is diamond shaped. A raven may grow to a length of 21 in. [52.5 cm]. It has a very heavy bill. The raven is a scavenger (see SCAVENGER). It feeds mainly on dead animals. Occasionally, it will kill and eat a small animal such as a rabbit, and it also eats acorns and insects. There are two species of ravens in North America. The common raven lives throughout Canada, the western United States and Mexico, and parts of the Appalachian Mountains in the eastern United States. The raven has been found farther north, nearer the North Pole, than any other bird. The smaller white-necked raven is found in Mexico and the southwestern United States.

See also CROW; PERCHING BIRD.

RAVEN

The raven is a large, black bird of the crow family. It feeds mainly on dead animals.

RAY

The marbled torpedo ray is a type of electric ray that can give a 60-volt electric shock.

RAY A ray is a saltwater fish. It is cartilaginous—that is, it does not have any true bones in its body (see FISH). It is closely related to the shark (see SHARK). A ray is a flat, pancake-shaped fish with a slender tail and broad, flat fins. When a ray swims through the water, it looks as if it is flying. There are many species of rays found in the oceans off North America. Included in that group are the electric rays, stingrays, eagle rays, manta rays, and skates (see ELECTRIC FISH; SKATE). Most rays live near the bottom of the ocean. They eat mollusks

and crustaceans (see CRUSTACEAN; MOLLUSCA). Some rays may exceed 20 ft. [6 m] in length. The huge devil ray, or manta ray, flaps its fins like wings as it glides through the surface layer and feeds on plankton. It can even break through the surface and fly for a short distance.

RAYON (rā′ŏn) Rayon is a material produced from the cellulose fiber of cotton or wood pulp (see CELLULOSE). Rayon is widely used to make industrial materials and textiles for clothing, upholstery, draperies, and other fabrics.

Various chemical methods are used to turn the cellulose into a thick liquid, from which rayon threads are made. The liquid cellulose is forced through very small openings in devices called spinnerets to form filaments (tiny threads). There are three main ways to make rayon.

The viscose process is the most common. In this process, cellulose in the form of wood pulp is soaked in a solution of sodium hydroxide. The soaked cellulose is put through presses that squeeze out the excess liquid. The cellulose is then

RAYON—Manufacture

Viscose rayon is made from wood pulp (cellulose), which is treated with sodium hydroxide before being shredded and aged. The cellulose crumbs are next treated with carbon disulfide and sodium hydroxide, and the viscose formed is forced through the holes of a spinneret in an acid bath to form rayon threads.

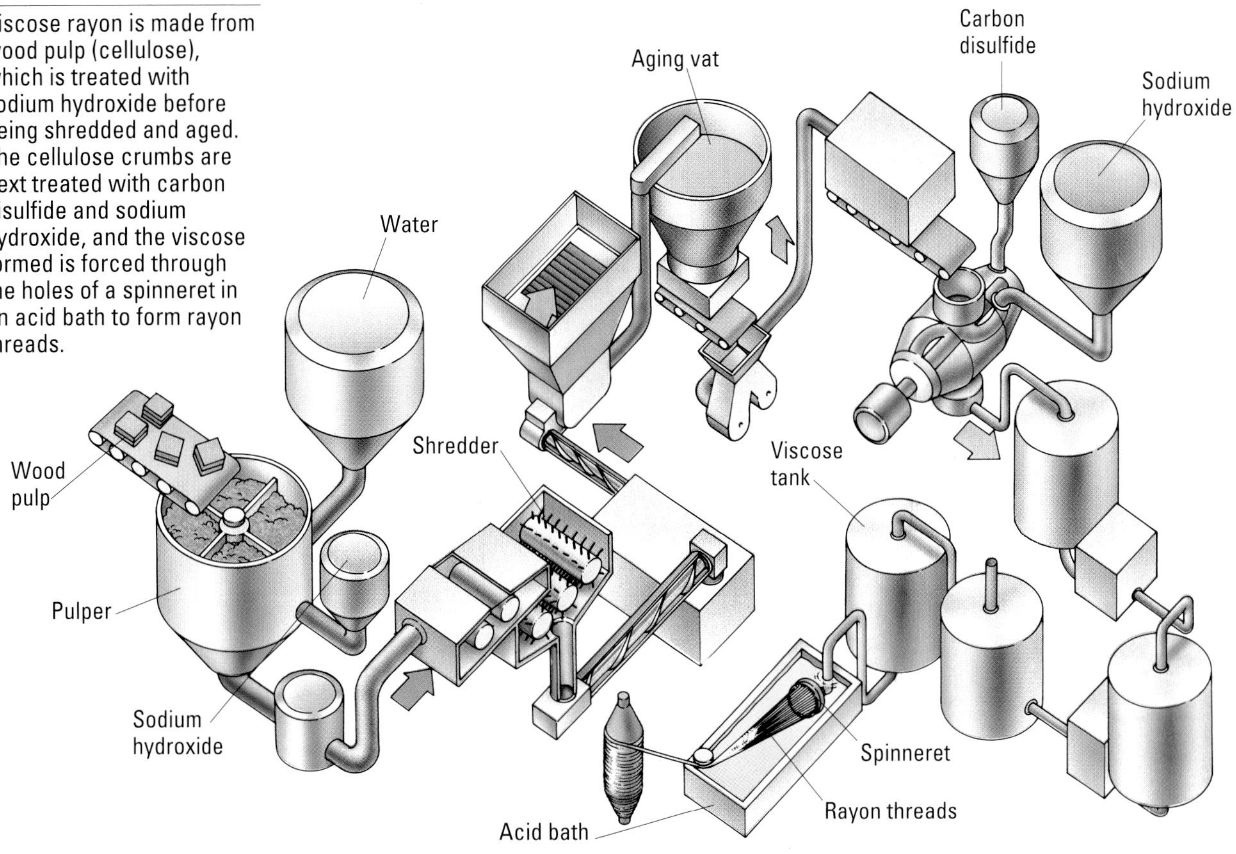

Water

Carbon disulfide

Aging vat

Sodium hydroxide

Wood pulp

Shredder

Viscose tank

Pulper

Sodium hydroxide

Spinneret

Rayon threads

Acid bath

shredded into crumbs. After aging at high temperatures, the crumbs are treated with carbon disulfide. Carbon disulfide turns these crumbs into cellulose xanthate. The crumbs are then dissolved in an alkali bath (see ALKALI). Next, pumps force the liquid through the tiny holes of a spinneret and into an acid to form rayon threads (see ACID).

Other methods for making rayon are the cuprammonium process and the acetate process. Rayon made by the acetate process is easily burned, and boiling takes out its shine. However, its fineness, texture, and dyeability make it desirable. *See also* CELLULOSE ACETATE.

REACTANCE (rē ăk′təns) In an electric circuit, certain components oppose the flow of current. This is called resistance (see CIRCUIT, ELECTRIC; CURRENT, ELECTRIC; RESISTANCE, ELECTRICAL). There are two types of current: direct current and alternating current. An alternating current flows first in one direction and then in the other. This is called a cycle. The number of cycles in a second is called the frequency of the current (see ALTERNATING CURRENT).

In some components, such as capacitors, the resistance depends on the frequency of the current. The resistance is then called the reactance. For a capacitor, the reactance increases as the frequency decreases (see CAPACITOR AND CAPACITANCE). Reactance, like resistance, is measured in units called ohms.
See also OHM.

REACTION, PRINCIPLE OF Mechanics is the branch of physics that studies the effects of forces on bodies. There are three very important laws of mechanics. They are called Newton's laws of motion (see DYNAMICS; MECHANICS; MOTION, LAWS OF). The third law of motion states that for every action there is an equal and opposite reaction. This means that forces always occur in pairs. For example, if a magnet attracts a piece of iron, then the piece of iron will also attract the magnet with a force that is equal in magnitude (size) but opposite in direction. When an object rests on the ground, the downwards contact force applied to the ground always produces an equal upwards reaction force.

This principle of reaction also applies to moving bodies. For example, when a bullet is fired from a gun, the gun recoils. The recoil is the reaction caused by the force that pushes the bullet out of the gun. Jet and rocket engines also work on the principle of reaction. Hot gases are thrust out the back of the engine. The force of the gases is the action. It produces a reaction in the opposite, forward direction. This reaction causes the jet or rocket to move forward.

REACTOR, NUCLEAR

A nuclear reactor is a device in which atoms are split in a controlled chain reaction in order to release energy (see CHAIN REACTION). This type of reaction is known as a fission reaction (see FISSION). Nuclear reactors use radioactive materials such as uranium-235, uranium-233, and plutonium-239 as fuel.

The chain reaction begins when the nucleus of a uranium-235 atom is hit by a neutron from the nucleus of another atom. This causes it to break into two roughly equal fragments. These release two or three very high-energy neutrons that then hit other atoms, causing them to break up and release more neutrons. The reaction produces heat, which is used to generate steam that spins a turbine. The turbine's shaft drives an electrical generator (see GENERATOR).

Nuclear reactors produce huge amounts of electricity around the world. They are sometimes also used to produce heat or serve as sources of neutrons used in scientific research (see NEUTRON).

Most nuclear reactors in the United States have a similar construction. A pressurized reaction vessel is housed within the radiation-proof containment shell. The vessel contains fissionable fuel and movable control rods. In these slow reactors, the vessel contains water. The water moderates, or slows, the liberated nuclear particles that begin the fission process. Without moderation, many of the particles would move too quickly to continue this type of nuclear reaction. When the vessel's control rods are withdrawn, the core becomes critical. The nuclear reaction occurs spontaneously, releasing an incredible amount of heat. This heat is absorbed by the pressurized water. The heated water is pumped into a heat exchanger unit. There, heat is transferred to a secondary water system. Water in this secondary system is vaporized and used to spin a steam turbine. After passing through the turbine, the steam is cooled in a sometimes elaborate condenser. After returning to its liquid state, the water

REACTOR DESIGNS

Three nuclear reactor designs are shown here. The common pressurized water reactor (right) has water under pressure as its coolant. In the advanced gas-cooled reactor (below), the coolant is carbon dioxide. The fast breeder reactor (below right) uses liquid sodium metal as its coolant. All types have heat exchangers in which the hot coolant boils water to make steam for driving turbine generators (to produce electricity).

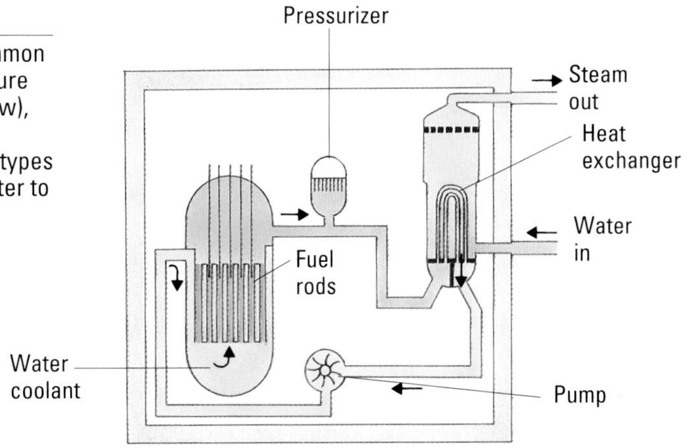

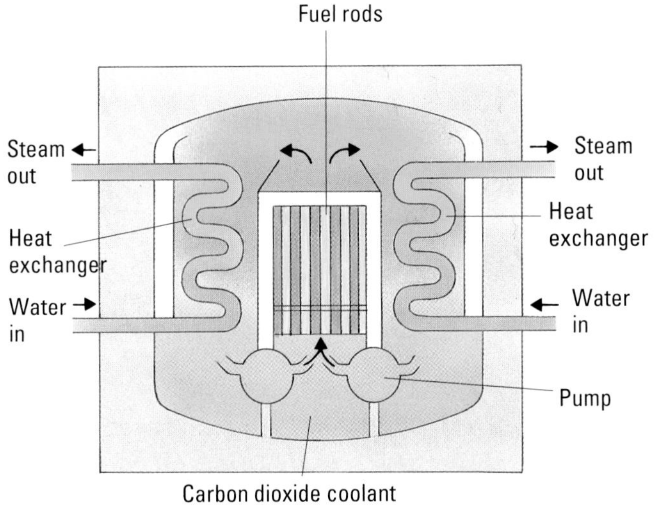

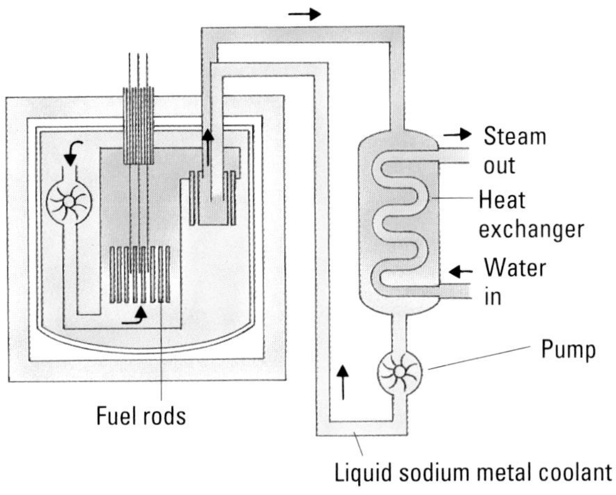

is pumped back into the reactor core, and the process repeats.

Some types of slow reactors are called breeder reactors. As the name implies, breeder reactors produce, or "breed," additional fuel materials. Another type of reactor is called a fast reactor. Unlike the slow reactors, these reactors contain no moderating materials. Instead of water, the fast reactors use a melted metal, such as sodium, to transfer heat energy.

At one time scientists thought that nuclear reactors could be used to produce limitless amounts of energy safely and at very low cost. Now people realize that there are still many safety problems to be solved. One serious unsolved problem is how to dispose of the waste (which is usually radioactive) produced by the reactors. Another problem is preventing radiation from escaping the plant (see RADIATION). If a fission reaction is not properly controlled, accidents can happen and radiation can be released into the surrounding area.

Serious accidents have already occurred. In 1979 the nuclear reactor at Three Mile Island in Harrisburg, Pennsylvania, failed, and some radioactive gases were released. Fortunately the health effects proved to be quite small. Much more nuclear radiation was released in 1986 when a reactor at Chernobyl in Ukraine caught fire and exploded (see CHERNOBYL). These safety problems have

made some people revise their thinking about the use of nuclear power.

See also NUCLEAR ENERGY.

BAD AND GOOD DESIGNS

In the RMBK reactor (below), the water coolant boils inside the reactor and steam is led off. A failure of this system caused a disastrous explosion at Chernobyl in Ukraine in 1986. In the Canadian CANDU reactor (bottom), a single loop of heavy water coolant produces steam in a heat exchanger.

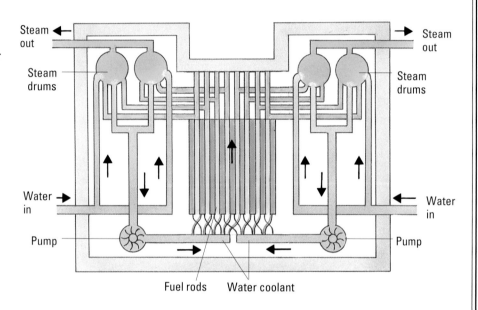

Steam out · Steam drums · Water in · Pump · Fuel rods · Water coolant

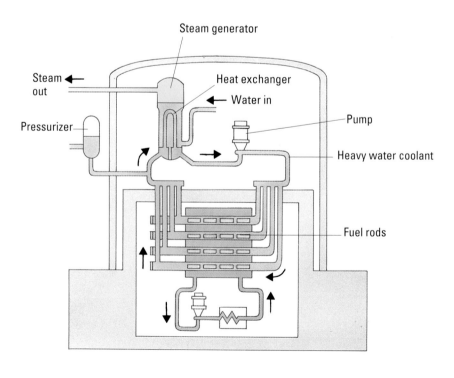

Steam generator · Heat exchanger · Water in · Pump · Heavy water coolant · Steam out · Pressurizer · Fuel rods

RECEPTACLE (rĭ sĕp′tə kəl) The receptacle is the swollen part at the top of a flower stalk. The petals and other parts of the flower are attached to it. In some fruits, such as apples, pears, and strawberries, the receptacle becomes the fleshy, edible part of the fruit. *See also* FLOWER; FRUIT; POME.

RECEPTOR (rĭ sĕp′tər) A receptor is a special nerve cell that responds to stimuli in the environment (see NERVE CELL; NERVOUS SYSTEM). Receptors are found in the sense organs of the body—the ears, eyes, nose, skin, and tongue—and within the body tissues. The receptors translate sounds, sights, position, and so on, into nerve impulses, or messages. The messages are then sent to the central nervous system through other nerve cells. The human eye, for example, has two major kinds of receptors in the retina. The retina is the light-sensitive part of the eye. These receptors are called rods and cones (see EYE AND VISION). The rods respond to light, but not to color (different wavelengths of light). The cones, on the other hand, do respond to color. They are called the color receptors.

RECESSIVE CHARACTER A recessive character is a characteristic of a plant or animal that does not always show up in an individual, even if the gene producing it is present. The characteristics of plants and animals are usually controlled by numerous genes, but some features can be controlled by a single pair of genes (see GENE). For example, the height of pea plants is controlled by two different genes. If the two chromosomes carrying the genes that control height both have "short" genes, the plant will be short, and if they both carry "tall" genes, the plant will be tall. If there is one "short" gene and one "tall" gene, the plant will still be tall. Although a "short" gene is present, it is masked by the "tall" gene. The "short" gene is called a recessive gene, and shortness in pea plants is called a recessive character. The "tall" gene is the dominant gene in this pea plant, so tallness is dominant over shortness (see DOMINANCE).
See also GENETICS; GENOTYPE; HEREDITY; MENDEL, GREGORY; PHENOTYPE.

RECORDING *Recording* has several meanings in science and technology. Most of these meanings come from the idea of making a record of observations, or data. For example, written data is a type of recording. Data that is input into a computer is also a type of recording (see COMPUTER). This data may be stored on a magnetic disk or tape, an optical disc, or a CD-ROM (Compact Disc Read-Only Memory). Optical discs (also called laser discs) and CD-ROMs can record a large amount of information including sounds (audio), text, photographs, and moving images (video).

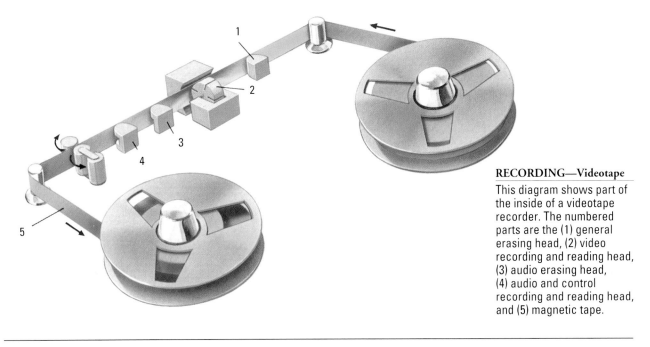

RECORDING—Videotape
This diagram shows part of the inside of a videotape recorder. The numbered parts are the (1) general erasing head, (2) video recording and reading head, (3) audio erasing head, (4) audio and control recording and reading head, and (5) magnetic tape.

RECORDING—Records and CD-ROMS
Sound can be recorded on magnetic tape or on vinyl records (below left). The storage space on a typical CD-ROM disc is allotted as shown (below right).

Photographs Audio
Video
Text
Program

Sound is also recorded as data (see SOUND RECORDING). Sound can be recorded on magnetic tape, such as reel-to-reel and cassette tape, and on vinyl records. Digital recording started to be used in the 1980s, when the first compact disc (CD) was produced. Compact discs give a very clear sound. Other types of digital recordings include the digital audio tape (DAT), the digital compact casette (DCC), and the minidisc (MD).

Images, such as those taken by photographic film, are also a type of data (see CAMERA). Camcorders and magnetic videotape record images and sound at the same time (see VIDEO RECORD-ING). A motion picture has its sound recorded as an optical or magnetic strip along the edge of the film (see MOTION PICTURE).

RECTIFIER (rĕk'tə fī'ər) A rectifier is a device that is used in electronic circuits. It lets an electric current flow through it easily in one direction. However, if the current tries to flow through it in the other direction, very little gets through. A rectifier is used for changing an alternating current into a direct current in electronic devices, such as televisions, that need some alternating current and some direct current (see ALTERNATING CURRENT; DIRECT CURRENT).

There are many different types of rectifiers. One type is called the metal rectifier. It consists of layers of copper disks. One side of each disk is coated with a layer of copper oxide. The disks are placed together so that one copper side is next to another copper side. Similarly, a copper oxide side is placed next to another copper oxide side. This gives a series of copper and copper oxide boundaries. The rectification takes place at these boundaries. A diode is a type of vacuum tube with two electrodes (see VACUUM TUBE). It allows current to flow in only one direction. It is often used as a rectifier.

RECYCLING (rē sī'klĭng) Recycling is the process of collecting wastes (materials that are left over after something has been produced or used) to regain materials in order to use them again. Recycled wastes provide materials for many new products. For example, recycled aluminum cans are used to make new cans and other aluminum products. Recycled paper is used in making new paper and insulation (see INSULATION). Recycled glass is used to make new glass products and even a tough material for street paving. Recycled motor oil is used as fuel oil in industry.

The interest in recycling has been steadily growing, partly because many cities in the United States are facing shortages of places to dispose of their waste. Many landfills are being closed due to concerns about the pollution they cause or because they are becoming full (see WASTE DISPOSAL). Many areas today have recycling centers. Some even have curbside pickup of recyclable products.

The recyclable items that are often sent to landfills include aluminum cans, glass containers, newspapers and other paper products, plastic products, and scrap metal. Besides saving landfill space, recycling also saves natural resources that would be used to make totally new products (see NATURAL RESOURCE). For example, recycling paper and paper products saves trees. Hundreds of thousands of trees could be saved each week if all newspapers were recycled.

Recycling metal reduces the amount of minerals that have to be dug. It also saves the landscape from being harmed by mining (see MINING). Recycling has many other advantages. It saves energy (see ENERGY). For example, recycling aluminum products and making them into new products uses 95 percent less energy than producing aluminum products from newly mined bauxite, from which aluminum is extracted. Recycling paper and making new paper products uses 60 percent less energy than manufacturing paper and paper products from newly cut timber. The amount of energy

saved from recycling a glass jar could be used to light a 100-watt bulb for four hours. Recycling also helps reduce the pollution that may be caused by improperly disposing of various wastes (see POLLUTION). For example, old batteries, paints, and motor oil contain poisonous substances. Improper disposal of these substances may cause water supplies to be contaminated.

In spite of all of these advantages, recycling faces many obstacles. For example, many wastes, such as plastic products, are difficult to recycle. Many plastic products are actually made up of many layers of different types of plastic. These layers are difficult to separate so they can be used again. Another problem is that consumers may not readily buy products made from recycled materials. For example, recycled paper is usually less white than most paper used in today's offices.

Much research is being done on recycling. For example, scientists are developing new products that can be made from recycled materials. They are researching different processes for recycling plastics. Communities are also educating their citizens about recycling. For example, some programs teach how food and yard scraps can be turned into compost for gardens.

See also COMPOST.

 PROJECT 70

RECYCLING

Many communities have recycling centers where people can take waste products. There are usually different containers for paper, glass (separated by color), and metals such as aluminum cans.

REDBUD The redbud is any of several species of trees and shrubs belonging to genus *Cercis* of the pea family (see PEA FAMILY). Redbuds can grow to about 40 ft. [12 m] tall and have smooth, reddish brown bark and hard wood. Clusters of pink or purple flowers bloom in the spring before the leaves grow. The leaves are simple and heart shaped (see LEAF). The seeds grow in pods (legumes) and are a source of food for wildlife. The trees are popular in parks and gardens.

REDBUD

Several kinds of trees and shrubs, all of which are members of the pea family, are called redbuds.

RED GIANT A red giant is any large, bright star with a relatively cool surface (see STAR). Red giants exist at a late stage in the life of a star such as the sun. When these stars run out of hydrogen fuel at their center, they expand and cool to form a red giant. Red giants usually have diameters between 10 and 100 times that of the sun. However, some red giants are larger. One of the largest stars, called Betelgeuse, is a red giant in the constellation of Orion. It has a diameter of 621 million mi. [1,000 million km], which is more than 730 times greater than the diameter of the sun. The matter inside a red giant is spread out over such a large volume that it is not much denser than the best vacuum that can be created in a laboratory. Red giants are bright

RED GIANT

This part of the night sky contains the constellation Orion (the Hunter). The bright star at the top left is Betelgeuse, a red giant that is 600 light-years from the earth.

because they are so large. However, their surface temperature is lower than that of the sun, which is about 3,100 to 4,900°F [1,700 to 2,700°C].

RED SHIFT Red shift is a type of Doppler effect seen in light from stars and galaxies (clusters of stars) that are moving away from us (see DOPPLER EFFECT). The dark lines of the absorption spectra (plural of *spectrum*) of this light are found to move toward the red end of the spectrum (see SPECTRUM). Red shift is used by astronomers to determine the distance of a star or galaxy from the earth and the speed at which it is moving.

Astronomers determine red shift by passing the light of a star or galaxy through an instrument called a spectroscope. The spectroscope separates the light into its different colors (see SPECTROSCOPE). Certain lines appear in the spectrum,

RED SHIFT

Astronomers use the red shift to determine the distance from Earth of stars and galaxies, such as the spiral galaxy pictured, and the speed at which they are moving.

caused by the absorption of radiation in the star's or stars' atmosphere. These lines will be shifted toward the violet end of the spectrum if the star or galaxy is approaching the earth. The lines will be shifted toward the red end of the spectrum if the star or galaxy is moving away from the earth.

Edwin Hubble, an American astronomer, determined that the greater the red shift, the more distant the star or galaxy and the greater its speed of motion away from the earth. A red shift is evident in all the galaxies beyond the Local Group (a group of about twenty nearby galaxies). If Hubble's interpretation of the red shift is correct, it not only indicates that the galaxies are moving away from the earth (and from one another) but also that the more distant galaxies are moving away at even greater speed. Scientists have thus concluded that the universe is now expanding.

See also GALAXY; HUBBLE, EDWIN POWELL; UNIVERSE.

REDWOOD The redwood is one of the largest trees in the world. It grows up to 340 ft. [103 m] tall and 25 ft. [7.6 m] thick. It belongs to the same family as the giant sequoia although it is placed in a different genus (see GIANT SEQUOIA). The redwood is an evergreen, with needlelike leaves. The fruit of the tree is a cone (see CONIFER; EVERGREEN). The wood of the redwood is red, soft, and resistant to water. It is often used to make lawn furniture and decks for swimming pools. The redwood grows in coastal California and Oregon,

REDWOOD

Redwood trees are some of the largest trees in the world. They grow in California and Oregon in parks, where they are protected from destruction.

where there are state and national parks to protect the giant tree.

See also NATIONAL PARK.

REED *Reed* is the common name for several large grasses that live in and around water (see GRASS FAMILY). They can be found throughout the world. The stems are largely hollow or filled with a watery pith (spongy tissue). The flowers grow in dense clusters at the tops of the stems (see INFLORESCENCE).

Common reed, belonging to the genus *Phragmites*, grows in and around shallow water in almost every part of the world. It forms dense

REED
Several kinds of grasses that grow in water are called reeds. Reeds are used to make thatched roofs, musical instruments, and baskets.

reed beds around some large lakes and also in many estuaries. Its stiff, smooth stems reach heights of 10 ft. [3 m]. They are sometimes hollowed out and used to make musical instruments. They are also used for basket making, but their main use is for making thatched roofs. Giant reed, which belongs to the genus *Arundo*, grows to a height of about 20 ft. [6 m] and is one of the largest of the true grasses. It is a native of the Mediterranean region, where it is widely planted to shelter delicate crops from the wind. Its canelike stems are used for fences and fishing rods and for shading the terraces and verandas of many Mediterranean houses. Panpipes were traditionally made from the stems, and the plant also yields the "reeds" used for the mouthpieces of clarinets and other wind instruments.

REED, WALTER (1851–1902)

REED, WALTER (1851–1902) Walter Reed was an American physician who proved that both typhoid fever and yellow fever can be spread by insects. As an army surgeon during the Spanish-American War (1898), Reed showed that flies carried the microorganism that causes typhoid fever (see MICROORGANISM; TYPHOID FEVER).

In 1900, as head of the U.S. Army Yellow Fever Commission, Reed was trying to control an epidemic among American soldiers in Cuba (see EPIDEMIC; YELLOW FEVER). Reed's commission conducted many experiments there. Eventually, they began testing a theory put forth by the Cuban physician Carlos Finlay that mosquitoes carried the microorganism that causes the disease. To confirm this, several soldiers and doctors volunteered to be bitten by the mosquitoes. Finlay's theory was proved to be true. For many years, Reed received all the credit for the theory. Finlay received credit for his contribution in 1954 (see FINLAY, CARLOS).

Once the carriers of typhoid and yellow fever had been identified, scientists were able to control the spread of the diseases by killing the insect carriers.

See also DISEASE; INFECTION.

REFLECTION OF LIGHT

REFLECTION OF LIGHT When light hits a surface, all or part of it bounces off the surface. This is called reflection. With some materials, such as clear glass, only part of the light is reflected. The rest passes through the material. With other materials, such as metals, nearly all the light is reflected from the surface.

The ray of light hitting a surface is called the incident ray. The ray that is reflected is called the reflected ray. The reflected ray obeys two simple laws. Imagine a line drawn at 90 degrees to the surface. This line is known as the normal. The normal and the incident and reflected rays all touch the surface at the same point. The normal and the incident and reflected rays all lie in the same plane.

This is the first law of reflection. The angle between the incident ray and the normal is called the angle of incidence. In the same way, the angle between the reflected ray and the normal is called the angle of reflection. The second law of reflection states that these two angles are always equal.

See also LIGHT; REFRACTION OF LIGHT.

PROJECT 43

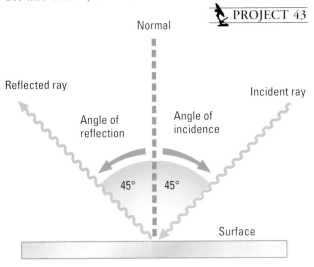

REFLECTION OF LIGHT

The angle between the incident ray (the ray of light hitting a surface) and the normal (an imaginary line drawn at a 90-degree angle to the surface) is the same as the angle between the reflected ray and the normal. This is the second law of reflection of light.

ACTIVITY *How to show reflection*

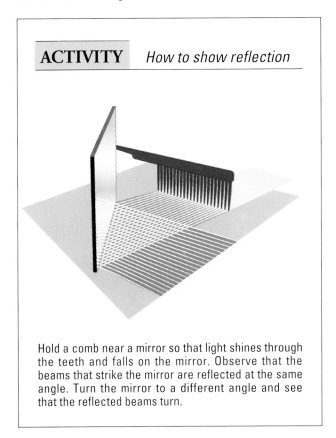

Hold a comb near a mirror so that light shines through the teeth and falls on the mirror. Observe that the beams that strike the mirror are reflected at the same angle. Turn the mirror to a different angle and see that the reflected beams turn.

REFLEX A reflex is an automatic action in response to a stimulus. For example, if a person accidentally touches a hot stove, he or she jerks his or her hand away before having time to think about what he or she is doing. In this example, the hot stove is the stimulus. The jerking away is the reflex, or response.

Reflexes such as the "pupil reflex" are quite common. If a bright light is directed at a person's eye, the pupil (opening) of the eye becomes smaller. If the light is taken away and the person's eyes are shaded, the pupil becomes larger again. The light or shade acts as the stimulus. The reaction of the pupil is the eye's response.

In its simplest form, four basic events are involved in a reflex—reception, conduction, transmission, and response. The stimulus is received by special nerve cells called receptors (see RECEPTOR). Energy from the stimulus is changed into nerve impulses, or messages, and conducted (carried) from the receptor to the central nervous system by sensory nerves. From the central nervous system, the nerve impulses are transmitted (sent) to the motor nerves. The motor nerves cause the muscles and glands to respond (act) (see NERVOUS SYSTEM).

Doctors often test a person's reflexes to make sure that various parts of the person's nervous system are working properly. The knee jerk reflex, also called the patellar reflex, is frequently tested. The doctor lightly strikes a tendon beneath the kneecap with a rubber hammer. This causes a reflex contraction of the muscles of the upper leg, which in turn causes the lower part of the leg to jerk upward suddenly. Such reflexes are called "unconditioned reflexes." All normal people and many other animals have unconditioned reflexes. These reflexes happen without special learning or experience.

Another type of reflex, the conditioned reflex, was believed by Ivan Pavlov to be the basis of learning (see PAVLOV, IVAN PETROVICH). However, most psychologists today believe that the mechanism of learning is much more complicated.

See also LEARNING AND MEMORY.　PROJECT 71

REFRACTION OF LIGHT Refraction of light is a change of direction in a ray of light as it passes from one substance to another. When a ray of light hits an object, some of it may pass through the surface. For example, light passes through glass. As a light ray passes from the air into the glass, it is bent—that is, it changes its direction. This is refraction. Imagine a line drawn from the surface into the substance. This line is at a 90° angle to the surface and meets it at the same point as the light ray. The line is called the normal. The ray can be bent either toward or away from the normal. When a ray passes from air into glass, it is bent toward the normal. When it passes out into air again, it is bent away from the normal. Another change happens when light passes from one substance to another. The speed of the light changes. As the light is bent toward the normal, it slows down. As the light is bent away from the normal, it is speeded up.

There are two basic laws of refraction. The ray that hits the surface is known as the incident ray. The first law states that the incident and refracted rays and the normal all lie in the same plane. The second law is called Snell's law. The angle between the incident ray and the normal is called the angle of incidence. The angle between the refracted ray and the normal is called the angle of refraction. Snell's law states that the sine of one of these

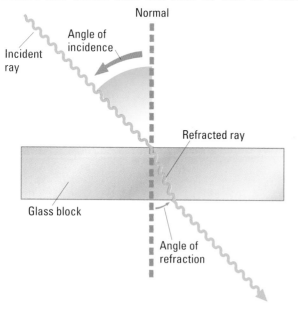

REFRACTION OF LIGHT

Refraction of light is a change of direction in a ray of light as it passes from one substance to another. When a ray of light hits an object, some of it may pass through the surface. As the ray passes through, it changes direction. This is refraction.

angles is proportional to the sine of the other angle (see TRIGONOMETRY). The sine of the angle of incidence divided by the sine of the angle of refraction is a constant. The size of the constant depends on the two materials that the light is passing through. It is called the refractive index between the two materials.
See also LIGHT; REFLECTION OF LIGHT.

 PROJECT 41

REFRIGERATION (rĭ frĭj′ər ā′shən) Refrigeration is the process of producing low temperatures by removing heat from a substance. Refrigeration is based on the second law of thermodynamics (see THERMODYNAMICS). This law implies that if two objects are at different temperatures, heat will flow naturally from the warmer object to the cooler object. Refrigeration is also based on the idea that when a gas becomes a liquid, it loses heat. When a liquid becomes a gas, it absorbs heat (see GAS; LIQUID).

Refrigeration often takes place in an insulated cabinet or room called a refrigerator (see INSULATION). Refrigerators are often used to store food in the home. Refrigerators can also be used to store other items, such as blood for transfusions, to keep them from spoiling.

In a home refrigerator, the substance that removes heat from another substance, such as warm food, is called the refrigerant. A refrigerant is a substance that evaporates (becomes a gas) and condenses (becomes a liquid) as a result of changes in pressure (see CONDENSATION; EVAPORATION). There are several kinds of refrigerants, including ice, carbon dioxide, and a chlorofluorocarbon (CFC) called freon (see CHLOROFLUOROCARBON). Because CFCs damage the protective ozone layer in the atmosphere, they are gradually being replaced by other types of refrigerants (see OZONE LAYER).

The cooling cycle in a home refrigerator begins when the liquid refrigerant leaves a kind of storage tank called a receiver. The liquid refrigerant travels through a pipe to a device called the refrigerant-control device. This device reduces the pressure of the liquid refrigerant as it enters the evaporator. The evaporator is actually a series of pipes that may line the walls of the refrigerator and/or the

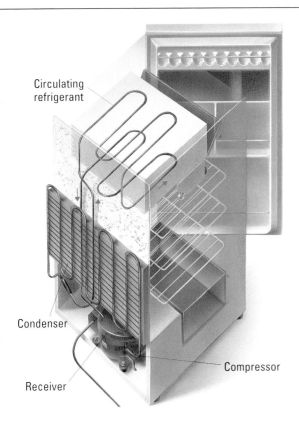

Circulating refrigerant

Condenser

Receiver

Compressor

REFRIGERATION

In a home refrigerator, heat is removed from the contents by an ice-cold refrigerant, which circulates in narrow pipes. The warmed liquid turns to a gas, which is cooled again on passing through an expansion valve. A compressor then turns the refrigerant back into a liquid.

compartment known as the freezer. Because the liquid refrigerant is now at low pressure, it evaporates and becomes a gas. During evaporation, the refrigerant becomes cooler. Therefore, heat moves toward the refrigerant. In other words, the refrigerant absorbs heat from within the refrigerator. This causes refrigeration. Another device called a compressor pumps the refrigerant, which is now a gas, into a condenser. The compressor also increases the pressure of the gas refrigerant. The increased pressure causes the gas refrigerant to turn back into a liquid in the condenser. As it does so, the refrigerant releases its heat outside the refrigerator. The liquid refrigerant then flows back to the receiver to start the cooling process again.

REGENERATION (rǐ jĕn′ə rā′shən) Regeneration is the ability of an organism to grow new body parts to replace lost or damaged ones. All organisms have at least some power of regeneration. However, it is most common in plants and lower animals. For example, many lawn owners try to control weeds by cutting them off at ground level. The remaining roots quickly regenerate new stems and leaves, however. The resulting plant may be even larger than the original. This principle is often used by gardeners who want to produce several plants that are exactly identical to an original one. They plant certain structures, such as leaves or pieces of stem, which then grow into new plants (see VEGETATIVE PROPAGATION).

Some lower animals, such as sponges, cnidarians (such as jellyfish), and simple worms, can be cut into several pieces, and each of these pieces will regenerate into a new organism. Starfish can regenerate lost arms. Lobsters and crayfish can regenerate lost claws, legs, and eyes. Insects can also regenerate lost limbs as long as the damage occurs before they reach maturity.

Regeneration among the vertebrates (animals with backbones) is more limited. Most bony fishes can regenerate lost fins. Fishes whose skeletons are made of cartilage, however, cannot. Many lizards and newts not only regenerate a lost tail, but may purposely break it off to escape from an enemy. Molting is also a form of regeneration (see MOLTING).

Although humans and other mammals cannot regenerate lost limbs or tails, they can replace hair, nails, and skin. In addition, mammals can repair broken bones and other damaged tissues. For example, if as much as 75 percent of a human liver is removed, the remaining tissue increases in size until it is as large as the original organ. Many other organs, such as lungs and kidneys, increase in size to replace lost or damaged tissues. If lost at an early age, the fingertip of a child will regenerate itself.

Sometimes, the tissues that an organism regenerates are different from the original tissues. Some arthropods (animals such as insects, spiders, crabs, and lobsters) replace an antenna with a leg or an eyestalk with an antenna. Frequently, the regenerated structure is smaller than the original. It usually functions well enough to replace the original, however. Sometimes, the new structure looks and functions like the original but differs in details (see ASEXUAL REPRODUCTION; REPRODUCTION).

REGENERATION
This damaged five-armed starfish is in the process of regenerating a lost arm.

The word *regeneration* is also used to describe the process by which a woodland or any other habitat regains its original condition after fire or other interference, such as tree felling.

REINDEER (rān′dîr′) The reindeer is a deer that lives in the cold, northern areas of Europe and Asia. It is usually considered to be the same species as the caribou of North America, although it is a different race or subspecies (see CARIBOU; DEER). The reindeer and caribou are the only deer in which both the males and females have antlers (see ANTLER). They also have large, broad hoofs that are well-suited for walking on the snow.

A reindeer may grow to 4 ft. [1.2 m] tall at the shoulder and weigh more than 330 lb. [150 kg]. It is usually gray or brown, with lighter fur on its belly. The reindeer has hard, stiff hairs covering a soft, thick underfur. Reindeer usually travel in large herds. They migrate (pass periodically from one region to another) southward into the forests in the winter and feed mostly on a lichen called reindeer moss (see LICHEN). In the summer, the herd moves northward to the tundras (treeless plains of northern regions), where the animals feed on lichens and grasses and on the dwarf shrubs.

Reindeer mate in the fall after the males have fought to gather large groups of females around them. After a pregnancy of about seven and a half months, the female gives birth to one or two calves. Most reindeer live for about fifteen years.

In many countries, reindeer have been domesticated. They are used as pack animals because they can carry or pull heavy loads without tiring easily. Reindeer also provide milk, meat, and hides.

Domesticated reindeer are kept in large numbers

REINDEER
Both male and female reindeer have antlers. Reindeer usually travel in herds. These animals were photographed in Svalbard (Spitsbergen), in the north of Norway.

by the Sami, or Lapps, a people of northern Norway, Sweden, and Finland and the Kola Peninsula of Russia. By about 1800, wild reindeer had been exterminated in Sweden. They have survived in the mountainous areas of southern Norway. Wild reindeer are also found in northern and eastern Finland. The natural enemies of reindeer include lynxes, wolves, and wolverines.

REINFORCED MATERIALS
Reinforced materials are materials that are strengthened by being combined with other stronger materials. For example, reinforced concrete is strengthened by embedding metal bars or metal wire into the wet concrete (see CONCRETE AND CEMENT). In another reinforced material called fiberglass, strong glass fibers are embedded into a polymer resin to make a material that is very strong, yet light (see FIBERGLASS; POLYMER). Polymer resin is also reinforced with strong carbon fibers to produce a reinforced material used to make aircraft bodies.

RELATIVE ATOMIC MASS
The relative atomic mass is the mass of one atom of an element divided by $1/12$ of the mass of one atom of carbon 12. Originally the mass of hydrogen, the lightest atom, was taken as the standard and the masses of all other atoms and molecules were compared with it. Now, by international agreement, one-twelfth of an atom of carbon 12 is taken as the standard mass.

Scientists use relative atomic masses when making calculations based on chemical equations. The symbol for relative atomic mass is A_r. Although the terms *molecular weight* and *atomic weight* are still in use, the correct terms are now *relative molecular mass* and *relative atomic mass*.
See also CHEMICAL FORMULAS AND EQUATIONS; ISOTOPE; RELATIVE MOLECULAR MASS.

RELATIVE DENSITY
The density of a substance is the amount of mass (matter) it contains for each unit of its volume (amount of space it occupies) (see DENSITY). Density is measured in pounds per cubic inch or foot, in grams per cubic centimeter, or in kilograms per cubic meter. The relative density, sometimes called the specific gravity, of a substance is its density divided by the density of a standard substance. Usually, water at 39°F [4°C] is used as the standard substance. If the relative density of a substance is less than 1, then the substance is less dense than water. Therefore, a substance with a relative density less than 1 floats on water. A few metals, such as sodium, do have a relative density of less than 1. Most metals, though, have a relative density much greater than 1. Gold, for example, has a relative density of about 19.

RELATIVE MOLECULAR MASS
The relative molecular mass is the mass of one molecule of substance divided by one-twelfth the mass of one atom of carbon 12. The symbol for relative molecular mass is M_r. Formula mass is used instead of molecular mass for substances that do not exist as molecules, for example, ionic compounds.
See also CHEMICAL FORMULAS AND EQUATIONS; ISOTOPE; RELATIVE ATOMIC MASS.

RELATIVITY
(rĕl′ə tĭv′ĭ tē) Relativity is a theory that describes what happens when objects move at very high speeds (near the speed of light), and how the force of gravity is produced. The theory of relativity was first presented by the German-American scientist Albert Einstein (see EINSTEIN, ALBERT). The theory is in two parts. The first part is called the special theory of relativity. It was published in 1905, when Einstein was only 26 years old.

The problem that concerned Einstein was whether or not the speed of light depends on the speed at which an observer is traveling. In the early 1900s, people believed that light traveled through a stationary (unmoving) medium called the ether. This imaginary ether was believed to fill all space. It was also thought that the speed of light relative to a moving observer could be calculated in the same way as the relative speeds of any two moving objects. For example, imagine two cars moving down the highway. One is traveling at 70 m.p.h. [112 kph] and the other at 50 m.p.h. [80 kph]. To passengers in the faster car, the slower car would seem to be traveling at 70 - 50 m.p.h. [112 - 80 kph],

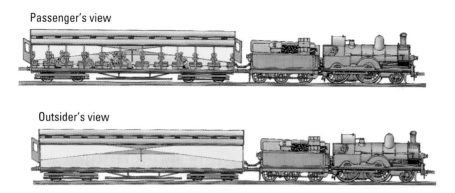

Passenger's view

Outsider's view

RELATIVITY

The railroad car (top left) has devices on the doors at each end that open them when the center light is turned on. People riding in the car see the doors open at exactly the same time. But somebody outside the car sees the back door open before the front door. This is because the back door travels forward toward the approaching light, whereas the front door moves away from the light.

or 20 m.p.h. [32 kph] as they drive past it. We say that the speed of the faster car relative to the slower car is 20 m.p.h. [32 kph]. However, relative to the earth, the faster car is traveling at 70 m.p.h. [112 kph]. In talking about relative speeds, it is necessary to say what the speed is relative to. Relative to the sun, for example, the cars are moving at almost 24 million m.p.h. [39 million kph].

Two American scientists, Albert Michelson and Edward Morley, carried out an experiment in 1887 to try to measure the speed of the earth through the ether (see MICHELSON, ALBERT ABRAHAM). To do this, they tried to compare the speed of light as measured in the direction of the earth's rotation with its speed at right angles to this direction. They found no difference. This result seemed completely unexplainable. It did not fit into the simple idea that scientists then had about relative speeds. The explanation was provided by Einstein. He realized that the idea of an ether is unnecessary. He also said that the speed of light always is the same, no matter how fast the observer is moving. Light's speed is always 186,282 mi. [299,792 km] per second. When talking about the speed of light, it is not necessary to say to what it is relative to. The speed of light is absolute.

This statement may not seem very important, but it had very important effects. In his special theory of relativity, Einstein showed that as bodies move faster, they increase in mass and also become shorter (see MASS). This follows mathematically from the statement that the speed of light is absolute.

These effects are only noticeable as the speed of light is approached. Cars on the freeway do

become heavier and shorter as they go faster, but the effect is very small. On the other hand, an electron traveling at 99 percent of the speed of light becomes seven times heavier than its mass when it is at rest (see ELECTRON). Einstein's theory shows that no body can actually travel at the speed of light. If it did, it would be infinitely heavy and have zero length. The increase in mass and decrease in length of a body as its speed increases led Einstein to the conclusion that mass (m) and energy (E) are different aspects of the same thing. They are related by the famous equation $E = mc^2$, where c^2 is the speed of light multiplied by itself. Nuclear energy and nuclear weapons both depend on this equation.

The second part of Einstein's theory is called the general theory of relativity. He published this in 1915. The special theory applies only to bodies moving at a constant speed. The general theory applies to bodies that are accelerating (see ACCELERATION). It deals principally with the way the force of gravity works (see GRAVITY). In his general theory, Einstein suggested that the force of gravity is a property of space and time. He showed that space becomes "curved" by the presence of mass. The motion of the stars and the planets is controlled by this curvature of space. Light rays, too, are bent by the curvature of space around a body that has mass. The theory has been proved to be correct by measuring the bending of light rays as they pass close to the sun.

Einstein's theory of relativity is one of the greatest achievements of the human mind. Einstein, like Isaac Newton, was one of the most creative scientists of all time.

RELAY A relay is a type of electrically controlled switch that is used to open or close an electric circuit (see CIRCUIT, ELECTRIC). A standard type of relay contains an electromagnet—a piece of metal that can be magnetized and demagnetized by electricity—along with sets of contacts that switch the current on and off. The magnet and the contacts are connected by an armature that works like a gate latch between them. It can shut or open contacts when the current flows through the coil. This is how the relay switches on and off. These types of relays require several watts of power to operate properly.

A second type of relay, known as a reed relay, was developed for use with modern switching systems that have been equipped with transistors. This type of relay operates at powers of a few tenths of a watt. A reed relay consists of two flat magnetic strips that are enclosed in a sealed capsule filled with an inert gas and placed inside a coil. When the coil is energized, an electromagnetic field is created. This causes the two strips to make contact and close the circuit so that power can flow. When the coil is deenergized, the field vanishes, and the strips spring apart, breaking the connection.

Many different types of relays are available for different applications. Reed relays are commonly used in modern telephone switching systems. Other types of relays are used in circuit breakers, computers, ignition systems, and various types of electrical and electronic equipment.

REM A rem is a unit of radiation whose biological effect is the same as one rad of X rays. A rad is a measurement of the amount of radiation absorbed by a substance. The rem takes into account the effect of different types of radiations on living tissue. *Rem* stands for "*r*adiation *e*quivalent in *m*an (or *m*ammal)." In many places, the rem has been replaced by the unit called the sievert. One sievert is equal to one hundred rems.
See also RADIATION; X RAY.

REMORA (rĕm′ər ə) A remora is a saltwater fish that belongs to the family Echeneidae. It has a sucker on the top of its head, which it uses to attach itself to sharks and other large fish. The remora does not hurt the larger fish—that is, its host. The remora just moves with the fish to which it is attached in order to eat scraps and small fish that its host misses. Eight species of remoras are found in North American waters, ranging from about 6 in. [15 cm] to 3 ft. [1 m] in length.

REMOTE CONTROL Remote control refers to the manipulation of a machine by an operator who is not in direct contact with it. The operator instead sends signals, such as radio waves or infrared rays, to a machine through a device called a control unit. The machine has a device called a receiver. The receiver interprets the signals and gives the information to one or more electric motors that control various functions of the machine (see INFRARED RAY; RADIO).

For example, model airplanes are sometimes operated by radio remote control. An operator uses a radio set to send radio signals to the airplane. The signals are then interpreted by the receiver. The airplane may then fly faster, slower, or even land, depending on the type of signal sent. The operator is in contact with the airplane by means of the radio. He or she does not actually touch the airplane to control it. On the other hand, if a person were guiding the airplane with a length of string, he or she would be in direct contact with the airplane. Model cars and trucks can be operated in the same way. The telephone also is operated by remote control. When a number is dialed, it causes another telephone to ring. The second telephone may be a long distance away. Many televisions and videocassette recorders have remote controls that operate using an infrared ray. A complex remote control system is used in some modern houses. In this system, all of the home's electronic appliances, such as the television, radio, thermostat, videocassette recorder, and washing machine, are operated through remote control. Control units are located in various rooms throughout the house.
See also AUTOMATION.

REMOTE SENSING Remote sensing is a way of gathering information about an object without actually touching it. To gather information, airplanes and satellites carry sensors designed to detect different forms of energy, such as temperature, radio waves, sound waves, or different wavelengths of light including visible light (see SENSOR). Information from the sensors is fed into a computer where it is processed to produce maps or pictures.

Remote sensing is a convenient and efficient way to study the surface of the earth and the oceans. The first modern remote-sensing satellite for civilian use was *Landsat 1*, launched in 1972. There are now five main remote-sensing satellites actively collecting data. Some include radar instruments that can collect images through cloud cover and at night. Remote-sensing images can be used to make very precise measurements of the shape of the earth's surface and to make detailed maps of roads and cities—some satellites can even "read" a car's license plate. Remote sensing can also be used to identify crops growing in fields, gather weather information, monitor the health and size of forests, help in the search for fuel and mineral deposits, study ocean currents, and measure the extent of the greenhouse effect which may be causing the earth's atmosphere to warm up (see GREENHOUSE EFFECT).

REPRODUCTION
Reproduction is the process by which an organism produces more organisms like itself. It is one of the characteristics of living things that makes them different from nonliving things (see LIFE). In order for a species to survive, it must reproduce.

There are two types of reproduction: asexual and sexual. In asexual reproduction, a new organism develops from structures produced by one parent (see ASEXUAL REPRODUCTION). Offspring produced by asexual reproduction are genetically identical to the parent. All types of asexual reproduction are based on the mitotic division of cells (see MITOSIS).

The most common type of asexual reproduction is binary fission. In binary fission, one organism splits into two new organisms. Some organisms produce asexual buds or spores, which develop into new organisms. Some break into several pieces,

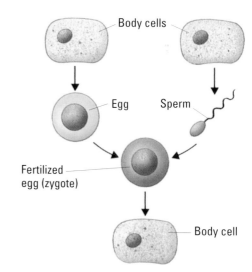

REPRODUCTION—Sexual

In sexual reproduction, sex cells, or gametes, are formed from body cells. The female gamete is an egg and the male gamete is a sperm. The two types of gametes combine at fertilization to produce a zygote, which develops into an embryo consisting of normal body cells.

each of which develops into a new organism. In animals, this is called fragmentation. In plants, it is part of vegetative propagation. Both fragmentation and vegetative propagation depend on regeneration for success (see REGENERATION).

In sexual reproduction, a new organism develops from two gametes (sex cells) that have joined together (see GAMETE). Usually, these gametes come from two different parents. In order for sexual reproduction to occur, a male gamete must fertilize a female gamete (see FERTILIZATION).

Each gamete contains half the number of chromosomes found in the parents' cells (see CHROMOSOME; MEIOSIS). When two gametes combine, the resulting zygote has the full number of chromosomes. A zygote develops into an embryo (see DIFFERENTIATION, CELLULAR; EMBRYO; ZYGOTE). The embryo develops into a baby, which eventually develops into an adult. The development of an organism is directed by information carried by DNA in the genes. The genes are located on the chromosomes (see DNA; GENE).

Most organisms have special reproductive structures that produce the gametes. The male gametes are usually called sperm. The female gametes are usually called ova (plural of *ovum*), or eggs. Some organisms produce both male and female gametes. They are called hermaphrodites (see HERMAPHRODITE). In some organisms, an egg develops into an adult without being fertilized (see PARTHENOGENESIS). Some organisms have two adult forms that alternate with each other in the life cycle. One reproduces sexually, and the other reproduces asexually (see ALTERNATION OF GENERATIONS; LIFE CYCLE).

Sexual reproduction in animals

All vertebrates (animals with backbones) and most invertebrates reproduce sexually. Among many invertebrates, fish, and amphibians, fertilization takes place outside the female's body. This is called external fertilization. In most cases, the female releases eggs and the male releases sperm nearby or on top of the eggs. In external fertilization, many of the gametes fail to pair up. For these reasons, animals that fertilize externally produce many more eggs than do animals that fertilize internally. The great numbers of eggs help ensure that at least some will be fertilized. As a rule, animals that fertilize externally provide little or no care for their offspring.

In most of the higher animals, fertilization takes place inside the body of the female. This is called internal fertilization. All reptiles, birds, and mammals reproduce by internal fertilization. In most cases, the male has an external structure, such as a penis, that can be placed inside the female's body. Sperm travels through the penis and is released inside the female's body in an opening that leads to the reproductive organs.

Most male birds, though they are internal fertilizers, do not have a penis. Instead, both males and females have a sack called a cloaca. The cloaca receives wastes as well as gametes. When birds mate, they place their cloacas close together. Sperm travels from the cloaca of the male into the cloaca of the female. Once inside the female's cloaca, the sperm locate and fertilize the eggs. Usually, when a bird lays eggs, they have been fertilized.

When eggs have been fertilized inside the female's body, they can develop in one of three ways. In viviparous animals, the eggs develop directly into embryos that grow into babies inside the mother's body. The babies receive nourishment from the mother's body and are born alive. All mammals except monotremes are viviparous (see MONOTREME). In oviparous animals, the fertilized eggs receive a protective covering or shell and are released to develop outside of the female's body. Monotremes, birds, and most reptiles are oviparous. In ovoviviparous animals, the eggs develop and hatch inside the mother's body, and the young are born alive almost immediately. While developing, the embryo receives nourishment from the yolk of the egg, and not directly from the mother. Some amphibians, fish, and reptiles are ovoviviparous.

REPRODUCTION—
Vertebrates

All vertebrates (animals with backbones), such as zebras and gazelles, and most invertebrates reproduce sexually. Fertilization may be internal or external, depending on the animal. In mammals, fertilization is internal.

This photograph, taken using a microscope, shows a human egg (large circle) at the moment of fertilization, surrounded by thousands of sperm.

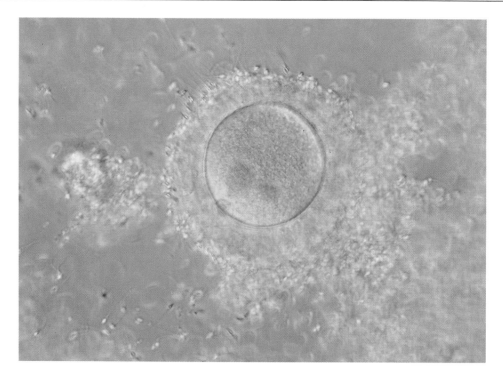

Human reproduction With some exceptions, fertilization in humans occurs after sexual intercourse. During sexual intercourse, a fluid called semen, containing millions of sperm, is released by the man into the vagina of the woman. This release of semen is called ejaculation.

Each sperm has a head and a flagellum, or whip-like tail. The sperm swim from the vagina, through the cervix, into the uterus. They continue through the uterus into the fallopian tubes. If an egg has been released from an ovary into a fallopian tube, it is likely that fertilization will occur. Normally, the woman's ovaries release one egg each month (see MENSTRUAL CYCLE). An egg lives for only about twelve hours after being released from the ovary. Sperm usually live for less than twenty-four hours. Therefore, there is a very limited time each month during which fertilization can occur.

When many sperm meet an egg, only one breaks through the egg's outer covering. This sperm is the one that fertilizes the egg. At this time, all the genetic characteristics are established, and development begins (see HEREDITY). Immediately after a sperm penetrates the egg, a chemical reaction takes place that prevents other sperm from penetrating. Since fertilization almost always occurs in one of the fallopian tubes, the fertilized egg travels down the tube into the uterus. Once in the uterus, it implants itself in the spongy, blood-rich uterine wall (see IMPLANTATION). Implantation usually occurs about three days after fertilization. This is the beginning of pregnancy (see PREGNANCY).

During pregnancy, the embryo develops a placenta and umbilical cord through which it receives food and oxygen and gets rid of carbon dioxide and other wastes. In addition, the placenta produces chemicals called hormones that ensure a healthy pregnancy (see HORMONE; PLACENTA; UMBILICAL CORD). By the end of the second month, the embryo has developed many recognizable human features. It is called a fetus. Growth and development continue throughout the pregnancy. During this time, many changes also occur in the mother's body. For example, special glands in the breasts get ready to produce milk. If the mother breast-feeds her child, these glands can continue producing milk for about two years. Otherwise, the glands become inactive within a few weeks after birth. Many of the changes that occur during pregnancy are controlled by hormones.

Normal pregnancy lasts about nine months. The birth of the baby ends pregnancy (see CHILDBIRTH). Childbirth is begun by a complex series of hormonal changes. These changes cause the muscles in the uterus to start contracting. These muscle contractions are called labor. As the baby's head begins pushing against the cervix, the contractions become stronger and more frequent. The mother also pushes with her abdominal muscles. Soon, the baby is pushed out of the uterus, through the vagina, and out of the mother's body. The uterus continues contracting until the afterbirth (placenta and other substances) is expelled through the vagina. After the baby has been born, its umbilical cord is cut and tied. In a few days, it dries up and drops off, leaving a scar called a navel.

Sometimes, a single fertilized egg will split in two, each half developing into an embryo. This results in identical twins. If the fertilized egg splits into three or more parts, each of which develops into an embryo, all the offspring will be identical. If two eggs are fertilized by two sperm, the result is fraternal twins. Sometimes, three or more eggs are each fertilized by different sperm. Fraternal offspring may look alike, but they are genetically different and may not all be of the same sex. Identical offspring, on the other hand, are genetically the same, and are always of the same sex.

In human beings, fertilization of an egg normally takes place in the body of the female. In 1978, however, a team of doctors in England reported the first successful instance of external fertilization (see TEST TUBE BABY). In this case, an egg was removed from the body of a woman and placed in a special nutrient substance. Sperm from the woman's husband were then placed near the egg. After the egg was fertilized, it was reinserted in the woman's body where it developed into a baby girl. In 1984, an embryo produced by external fertilization was frozen for two months and then successfully implanted in an Australian woman. Such procedures, and ones similar to them, are successful in many cases, but remain the subject of controversy.

Sexual reproduction in plants

Most plants have reproductive structures located in flowers (see FLOWER). The male part of a flower is called a stamen. A part of the stamen called the anther produces pollen (see POLLEN). The pollen produces male gametes. The female part of a flower is called a pistil. A part of the pistil called the ovary produces one or more ovules. Ovules produce female gametes. Pollen is carried from a stamen to a pistil in different ways. This transfer of pollen is called pollination (see POLLINATION). After a male gamete from a pollen grain has fertilized a female gamete in an ovule, the flower usually changes. The petals die. The fertilized egg becomes an embryo. The ovule becomes a seed (see SEED). The ovary becomes a fruit (see FRUIT). The seeds are dispersed when they become mature (see DISPERSION OF PLANTS). Each seed may germinate (sprout) and grow into a new plant (see GERMINATION).

Many plants do not have flowers. Some have cones which, like flowers, are reproductive structures that produce and scatter seeds. Many lower plants, such as ferns, mosses, liverworts, and hornworts (in addition to some species of algae and fungi, which are not in the plant kingdom), produce antheridia (plural of *antheridium*) and archegonia (plural of *archegonium*). An antheridium is the male reproductive structure (see ANTHERIDIUM). It produces mobile sperm. The archegonium is the female reproductive structure (see ARCHEGONIUM). Because the reproduction of organisms in the kingdoms Fungi, Monera, and Protista is so varied, it is discussed in detail in other articles.

See also ALTERNATION OF GENERATIONS; BACTERIA; CONTRACEPTION; FUNGUS; PROTOZOA; REPRODUCTIVE SYSTEM; SEX.

REPRODUCTIVE SYSTEM The reproductive system is a group of body organs that do the work of reproduction (the process by which an organism produces more organisms like itself). Most organisms (living things) are able to reproduce sexually. Most species have male organisms and female organisms. Male organisms produce male gametes, or sperm. Female organisms produce female gametes, or eggs (also called *ova,* which is the plural of *ovum*). Some organisms produce both male and female gametes (see HERMAPHRODITE). Human beings, however, are either male or female, with specialized structures for reproduction. This article discusses the human male and female reproductive systems.

Male reproductive system Human males have sex organs that are mostly outside of the body. *(Genitals* is another term for sex organs, particularly those that are external). The penis is located in the front of the body between the legs. Behind the penis is the scrotum, a sac that is made of skin. Inside the scrotum are two small, egg-shaped structures called testicles, or testes (see TESTICLE). During the reproductive life of a man, the testicles produce millions of sperm every day.

Sperm are stored in the testicles and in the epididymis, a tube that rests on top of each testicle. Each epididymis leads to a vas deferens. Each vas deferens is a tube that carries sperm from the epididymis to the urethra. The urethra is a tube that goes from the bladder, through the penis, to the outside of the body. Before sperm enter the urethra, they are mixed with a whitish fluid from the prostate gland and from structures called the seminal vesicles (see PROSTATE). This fluid is designed to help the sperm live and travel once they are deposited inside the female's vagina. The fluid, when combined with sperm, is called semen. Semen leaves the male's body through the urethra, as does urine from the bladder, but always at different times.

Female reproductive system The organs of a human female that are directly involved in reproduction are located inside her body. Eggs are produced in the ovaries (see OVARY). The ovaries are a pair of small, walnut-shaped organs near the front of the abdomen. Each month, one ovary releases an egg. This is called ovulation. The egg enters one of the fallopian tubes. The fallopian tubes are a pair of tubes that lead from the ovaries to the uterus. The tubes are lined with hairlike structures called cilia, which wave back and forth and create a flow that carries the egg toward the uterus. The uterus is a hollow organ that is shaped like an upside-down pear (see UTERUS). It is in the uterus that a fertilized egg will develop into a baby. The uterus opens at the bottom in a necklike structure called the cervix. The cervix leads to the vagina. The vagina is a narrow canal that opens to the outside. The external part of the vagina is called the vulva. The vulva protects the vagina and is made up of folds of skin called labia.

Each month, the uterus prepares for the arrival of a fertilized egg. If an egg is fertilized, it is usually fertilized in a fallopian tube. It then travels into the uterus, where it implants in the thickened, blood-rich uterine lining (see IMPLANTATION). If the egg is not fertilized, the thickened lining of the uterus is no longer needed. It breaks away and flows through the vagina in a process called menstruation (see MENSTRUAL CYCLE). The menstrual cycle is controlled by hormones. *See also* HORMONE; REPRODUCTION; SEX.

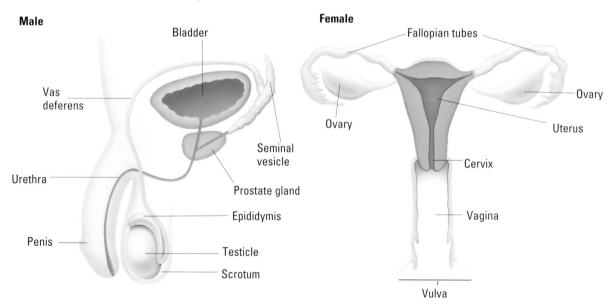

Male
- Bladder
- Vas deferens
- Seminal vesicle
- Urethra
- Prostate gland
- Epididymis
- Penis
- Testicle
- Scrotum

Female
- Fallopian tubes
- Ovary
- Ovary
- Uterus
- Cervix
- Vagina
- Vulva

REPRODUCTIVE SYSTEM
The diagrams show male and female human reproductive systems.

A reptile is an animal that belongs to the class Reptilia. The class includes the alligators, caimans, crocodiles, lizards, snakes, worm lizards, and turtles (see ALLIGATOR; CROCODILE; LIZARD; SNAKE; TURTLE). The class also includes the tuatara, which lives on islands off the coast of New Zealand. Tuataras look like lizards but are more closely related to the reptiles known as dinosaurs, which are now extinct (see DINOSAUR).

All reptiles have several things in common. They have dry, scaly skin; a backbone; a bony skeleton; lungs; and usually two pairs of limbs. Although snakes do not have any fully developed limbs, their skeletons have the remnants of four limbs that never develop. Nearly all reptiles lay eggs, though some give birth to live young.

All reptiles are ectothermic, or cold-blooded (see COLD-BLOODED ANIMAL). Their body temperature varies with that of the surrounding environment and is rarely much different from it. The animals are able to control their body temperature only by moving into the sun or shade. Reptiles that live in northern lands where winter temperatures drop to freezing must hibernate to stay alive (see HIBERNATION). Although reptiles are found in nearly all areas on Earth, they are most plentiful in the tropical regions, which do not have cold winters.

There are about six thousand species of reptiles. Most species live on land, but some live in fresh or salt water. Reptiles range in length from 2 in. [5 cm] to 31 ft. [10 m]. The smallest reptiles are lizards found in tropical regions. The longest reptile is the regal python, a snake. Some crocodiles have been measured at 30 ft. [9 m] in length and, with weights well over 1,000 lb. [445 kg], they are among the heaviest of all living reptiles. Some leatherback turtles also weigh over 1,000 lb. [445 kg].

Reptiles first appeared about 300 million years ago. They evolved from the amphibians (see AMPHIBIAN). Amphibians breathe largely through their skin, which must stay wet, so they have to live near water. Reptiles rely entirely on their lungs for breathing and they have tougher, waterproof skins. Also, reptiles' eggs—unlike those of amphibians—are surrounded by a hard protective shell, so they

EVOLUTION

Reptiles first evolved from amphibians about 300 million years ago. All the main groups of reptiles we know today were already in existence 135 million years ago.

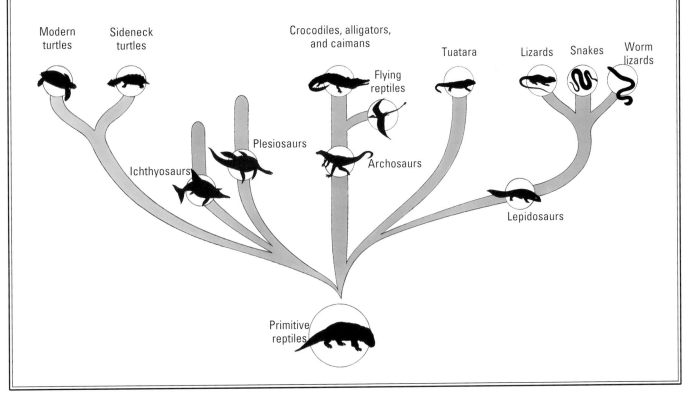

1625

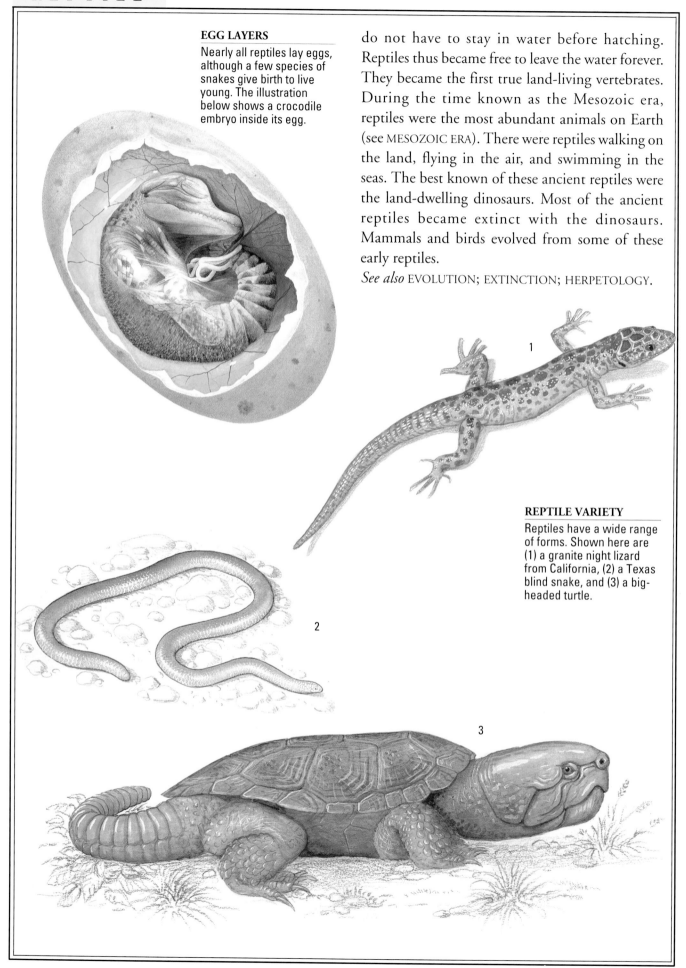

EGG LAYERS

Nearly all reptiles lay eggs, although a few species of snakes give birth to live young. The illustration below shows a crocodile embryo inside its egg.

do not have to stay in water before hatching. Reptiles thus became free to leave the water forever. They became the first true land-living vertebrates. During the time known as the Mesozoic era, reptiles were the most abundant animals on Earth (see MESOZOIC ERA). There were reptiles walking on the land, flying in the air, and swimming in the seas. The best known of these ancient reptiles were the land-dwelling dinosaurs. Most of the ancient reptiles became extinct with the dinosaurs. Mammals and birds evolved from some of these early reptiles.

See also EVOLUTION; EXTINCTION; HERPETOLOGY.

1

REPTILE VARIETY

Reptiles have a wide range of forms. Shown here are (1) a granite night lizard from California, (2) a Texas blind snake, and (3) a big-headed turtle.

2

3

RESERVOIR (rĕz'ər vwär') A reservoir is a place where large amounts of water are stored for a long time. Reservoirs have several uses. For example, the water may be used for irrigation, for drinking, to provide hydroelectric power, or for recreational purposes, such as boating or fishing (see HYDRO-ELECTRIC POWER; IRRIGATION).

Reservoirs can be either natural or artificial. A lake is an example of a natural reservoir. An aquifer is a natural reservoir that is underground. An artificial reservoir is generally made by building a dam on a river (see AQUIFER; DAM). The damming of a river to make a reservoir can harm various organisms (see ECOLOGY). For example, the organisms that lived in the river, which was a flowing body of water, may not be able to survive in a body of water that stands still. Also, the organisms that lived in the once-dry area now covered by water may not be able to survive. Because of such changes, scientists study carefully what effects the possible creation of reservoirs will have on an area.

RESERVOIR

Reservoirs are constructed for various purposes. Water collected in them can be used for drinking, irrigation, hydroelectric power, and recreation.

RESIN (rĕz'ĭn) Natural resins form a group of vegetable substances used in making such products as soaps, medicines, paints, and varnishes. Natural resins are obtained in three basic ways. Some flow from plants as a result of wounds, such as in pine trees. Some are removed from wood by solvents (substances that dissolve other substances). Others, namely fossil resins (such as amber), are found with the preserved remains of plants and animals (see FOSSIL). In an unusual way, one insect produces a resin that is called lac (see SHELLAC).

Resins do not dissolve in water, though soft resins can dissolve in ether or benzene. Hard resins, after heating, may be dissolved in vegetable oils. Gum resins are usually soft and sticky. Gum resins such as aloe, myrrh, and the gum of the balsam tree are often used in medicines. Rosin is a resin that is used in soap, paints, and varnishes. Other resins combined with certain oils are used in tar and turpentine.

In manufacturing, natural resins have largely been replaced by synthetic (human-made) resins. Synthetic resins form a large group of chemical compounds. This group includes many of the common plastics (see PLASTIC). Synthetic resins are products prepared by chemical reactions. They

may be made as films or fibers or molded into practically any shape. These compounds are used in paints and adhesives and as coatings on metal, cloth, and paper.

Synthetic resins are made up of many simple molecules linked together to form large, complex molecules called polymers (see POLYMER). The nature of a synthetic resin is determined by the chemicals it contains and by the pattern of the new molecules. Petroleum, limestone, salt, water, and air are often used to make synthetic resins. Complicated chemical processes change these materials into a variety of chemicals, such as alcohol, ethylene, and ammonia. These substances are then combined in various ways to form the complex molecules of the synthetic resins. Manufacturers may then change some of the properties of these resins by adding fillers, colors, or other materials.

RESIN

Natural resins are used in many products, such as soap, paint, and varnish. Here resin is being collected from a cut made in the wood of a pine tree.

RESISTANCE, ELECTRICAL
The electrical resistance of part of an electric circuit is a measurement of how difficult it is to pass a current through that part (see CIRCUIT, ELECTRIC; CURRENT, ELECTRIC). Substances such as metals have a low resistance. They are good conductors of electricity (see CONDUCTION OF ELECTRICITY). Carbon is a nonmetal that conducts electricity. It has a higher resistance than metals. Many other nonmetals have extremely high resistance. If the resistance is so high that current will not pass, the substance is a nonconductor, or insulator. Materials such as glass, plastics, and rubber are used as insulators because of their resistance to electric current.

Resistance is measured in units called ohms (see OHM). It can be calculated from the voltage, or potential difference, applied to the conductor, divided by the current that it causes to flow (see POTENTIAL; VOLT). If a potential difference of six volts produces a current of three amperes in a piece of wire, the wire has a resistance of two ohms (see AMPERE; OHM'S LAW). The symbol for ohm is Ω.

The longer a piece of wire, the greater its resistance. The thicker the wire, the less its resistance. By drawing a solid lump of copper out into a fine wire, its resistance can be increased many thousands of times, even though it is still the same quantity of copper. In a wire or bar that has a uniform cross section, the resistance (R) is given by the formula $R = pl/A$, where p is the resistivity of the conductor, l is the length, and A is the area of the cross section. Resistivity depends on the material that the conductor is made of, not on the shape of the conductor.

The resistivity of a substance changes with temperature. In most metals, heating produces increased resistivity. In many nonmetals and semiconductors, heating decreases the resistivity (see SEMICONDUCTOR). When an electric current flows through a resistance, some electric energy is always converted into heat. **PROJECT 31**

RESISTOR
(rĭ zĭs′tər) A resistor is a component in an electric circuit (see CIRCUIT, ELECTRIC). It is a part of the circuit designed to have a known amount of resistance to the passage of an electric

current (see CURRENT, ELECTRIC; RESISTANCE, ELECTRICAL). Resistance is measured in units called ohms (see OHM). A resistor that has a resistance of only a few ohms allows electricity to flow easily through it. A resistor with resistance of thousands or even millions of ohms needs a very high voltage (potential difference) to push an electric current through it (see POTENTIAL; VOLT).

Resistors are specially made for different purposes. They are used to adjust the voltage and current in the circuits of radio and television receivers, calculators, computers, and many other kinds of electrical equipment. Resistors may be made of coils of fine wire or of cylinders of carbon mixed with other substances. Fixed-resistance resistors are made in a range of different values. There is a color code to indicate different values. This is often painted on a resistor in bands or stripes of color. It shows the resistance in ohms.

A potentiometer is a variable resistor, or device for varying the resistance in an electric circuit. It consists of a contact that can be moved along a resistance wire or a circular track of a carbon resistance compound. By adjusting the point of contact, the amount of resistance through which the current has to pass can be varied. Variable resistors are used in radios, television sets, and other electronic equipment. A rheostat is a similar device. It is usually designed to adjust larger currents in circuits. Dimming controls for the lights in theaters or in the home may be forms of a rheostat. **PROJECT 31**

RESONANCE (rĕz′ə nəns) Many objects are naturally inclined to vibrate at a particular frequency. Vibrations of that frequency coming from a separate source can cause such objects to resonate. Resonance is the increase in the size of a vibration in a vibrating object. Frequency is the number of vibrations per minute (see FREQUENCY).

Objects that can be made to vibrate all have one or more natural frequencies of vibration. A beverage glass flicked with a fingernail will give out a musical note of a particular frequency. Each string of a guitar gives out a note that corresponds to its own natural frequency. Besides the main frequency, other notes are also given out. These correspond to frequencies that are simple multiples of the main frequency. They are called harmonics, or overtones (see HARMONICS).

When vibrations are passed into an object at its natural frequency, they are picked up very strongly. The vibrations build up to a maximum amplitude (see AMPLITUDE). When this happens in an object such as a drum, the object is said to resonate, and the effect is called resonance.

Certain opera singers have claimed to shatter glasses by singing notes that correspond to the resonant frequencies of the glass. The vibrations build up to such an amplitude that the glass shakes to pieces. The effect can be produced when a voice is amplified through a loudspeaker at the appropriate frequency (see LOUDSPEAKER).

Resonance can produce problems in bridges. If they are made to vibrate at their natural frequency, they may move so violently that they break up. Fortunately, the natural frequency of bridges is very low. It takes very unusual circumstances to make them resonate. However, strong winds have been known to vibrate suspension bridges to the point of destruction. To prevent the effect of resonance, soldiers marching over bridges are often ordered to

RESONANCE
The shape of a drum makes it resonate when struck, thus amplifying the sounds it makes.

break step so that regular vibrations from their feet cannot build up.

In electricity, resonance is also important. An electric circuit has a particular frequency to which it responds. The frequency is decided by the electric resistance and capacity of the circuit (see CIRCUIT, ELECTRIC; RESISTANCE, ELECTRICAL). An electric circuit can be made to respond to a desired frequency by varying the values of the components in it. This is called tuning the circuit to that frequency. Radio and television transmitters and receivers have circuits tuned to send and receive radio waves of various frequencies.

In chemistry, resonance has a different meaning, though vibration is still involved. In certain chemical compounds, the electrons that hold the atoms of different elements together in molecules can be thought of as constantly changing position. They oscillate, or vibrate, between different parts of each molecule, altering the bonds between the atoms (see ATOM; COMPOUND; ELEMENT; MOLECULE). Because of this, no true single structure can be drawn to represent a molecule of such a substance. There is only an "average" structure, which shows one set of alternatives. Such compounds are called resonance hybrids.

The molecule of benzene shows resonance (see BENZENE). It has a ring of six carbon atoms. They are linked by alternate single and double bonds. However, the electrons are oscillating between different atoms. At one instant, the bond between a particular pair of atoms is a single bond. In the next instant, it is a double bond. Then it goes back to a single bond, and so on. The change occurs constantly between all the pairs of carbon atoms in the benzene molecule. **PROJECT 47, 54**

RESOURCE EXPLOITATION People rely greatly on many types of resources found in nature. These include materials found in the earth's crust, such as minerals, soil, oil, gas, and coal, or resources found on the earth's surface, such as water. Sunlight and wind in the earth's atmosphere are also resources. These resources can be used in many different ways to provide people with energy, food, and raw materials to produce goods.

Resource exploitation involves finding the best and most efficient way to make use of natural resources (see NATURAL RESOURCE). Scientists and engineers involved in resource exploitation must consider many things, including the fact that many resources are nonrenewable and that poor use of others can cause pollution (see NONRENEWABLE RESOURCES; POLLUTION). They also have to consider how to get the most out of a resource in an economical way. **PROJECT 34, 70**

RESOURCE EXPLOITATION

Hot water and steam from below the ground—forms of geothermal energy—are natural resources. Here they are being exploited at a geothermal power station in Iceland.

Respiration (rĕs´pə rā´shən) is the process by which an organism breaks down food molecules in the presence of oxygen, changing food energy into a form that can be used by the cells. The end products of respiration are carbon dioxide and water, both of which are considered wastes.

Most organisms, called aerobes, get and use oxygen from the air (see AEROBE). Some organisms, however, are unable to use oxygen from the air (see ANAEROBE). Instead, anaerobes get their energy by breaking down compounds in the anaerobic process of fermentation (see FERMENTATION).

All organisms rely on food as their major source of energy. Some organisms, particularly plants, produce their own food (see PHOTOSYNTHESIS). Other organisms must get their food from other sources. Once such an organism has the required food, the food is broken down into smaller components. This process is called digestion (see DIGESTION). In digestion, enzymes help change protein into amino acids, fats into fatty acids and glycerol, and carbohydrates into simple sugars. In these forms, the components of food, called nutrients, can be absorbed and transported to the cells, where respiration occurs.

Stages of respiration Respiration has two major stages: external and internal, or cellular. In external respiration, there is an exchange of gases

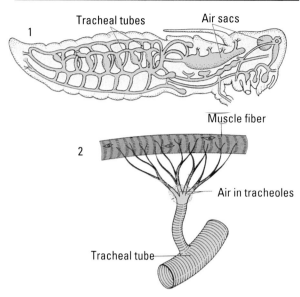

INSECT

(1) Inside an insect is a branching network of tracheal tubes and air sacs. (2) The tubes divide many times to become very fine tracheoles, which pass oxygen to the muscles and other parts of the body.

between the organism and its environment. Oxygen enters the organism, and carbon dioxide leaves it. In one-celled organisms, this exchange is by simple diffusion through the surface (see DIFFUSION). Diffusion is also used by many lower invertebrates (animals without backbones) and plants. Most plants, however, have openings called stomata through which air moves in and out of the organism. Some arthropods, such as insects, have tiny holes (spiracles) along the body (see SPIRACLE). Each spiracle opens into a branching tube that

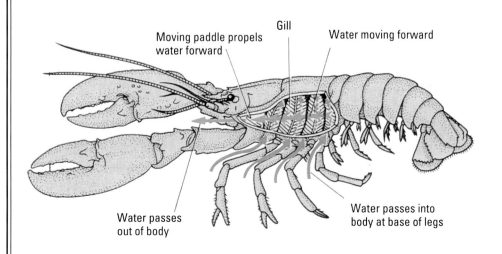

CRUSTACEAN

An aquatic crustacean, such as the lobster (left), has featherlike gills for breathing. Water is drawn in at the base of the legs, passed over the gills, and pumped out of the body.

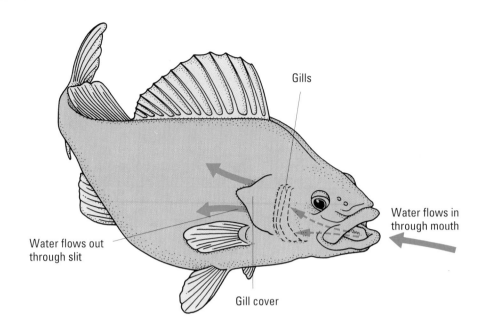

FISH

When a fish breathes (left), water flows in through its mouth and over the gills, arranged in four arches on each side of the head. The gills remove oxygen from the water, which then flows out through a slit behind the gill cover.

Gills

Water flows in through mouth

Water flows out through slit

Gill cover

leads to the cells. Most larger animals rely on diffusion through thin, moist membranes in a particular part of the body (see MEMBRANE). Since these membranes are very delicate, they are usually inside the animal's body and are protected in some way. Fish have gills, but land-living vertebrates and some land-living mollusks have lungs (see GILLS; LUNG). In animals, external respiration is also called breathing.

Oxygen passes through the gill or lung membranes and into the blood. Once it has entered the blood, it is transported to the cells where it will be used. This transport is also involved in taking carbon dioxide from the cells back to the gills or lungs where it can be removed from the organism during external respiration (see CIRCULATORY SYSTEM).

Cellular, or internal, respiration is the process that actually releases the energy stored in food and stores it for future use in chemical substances such as adenosine triphosphate (ATP) (see ATP). Cellular respiration involves a series of complex chemical reactions called glycolysis and the Krebs cycle. Each of these reactions involves a special enzyme (see ENZYME). In most cells, these enzymes are in the mitochondria (see MITOCHONDRIA). In some microorganisms, however, the enzymes are attached to the cell membrane, and respiration occurs there (see CELL).

Glycolysis is a series of reactions in which a glucose (sugar) molecule is changed into two pyruvic acid molecules, releasing a small amount of energy. In aerobes, the pyruvic acid molecules enter into the next series of reactions, the Krebs cycle (see KREBS CYCLE). The end products of the Krebs cycle are much energy, carbon dioxide, and water. Throughout the Krebs cycle and glycolysis, the energy that is released is used to change low-energy adenosine diphosphate (ADP) into high energy ATP. The chemical reaction that summarizes respiration is:

$$C_6H_{12}O_6 + 6\,O_2 \longrightarrow$$
$$6\,CO_2 + 6\,H_2O + \text{Energy (36 ATP)}$$

$C_6H_{12}O_6$ is glucose. O_2 is oxygen. CO_2 is carbon dioxide. H_2O is water. If there is not enough oxygen, there will not be enough ATP produced to meet all of the organism's energy needs. The organism may turn to the anaerobic process of fermentation for a time. If the lack of oxygen continues for more than a few minutes, however, the result will be suffocation. Some chemicals can block one or more of the reactions of respiration. For example, cyanide is a poison that causes death by blocking one part of respiration.

See also METABOLISM; RESPIRATORY SYSTEM.